A HISTORY

OF THE

CARTOGRAPHY

OF RUSSIA

UP TO

1600

LEO BAGROW

A HISTORY
OF THE
CARTOGRAPHY
OF RUSSIA
UP TO
1600

EDITED BY

HENRY W.
CASTNER

The Walker Press

Wolfe Island, Ontario

Published in Canada by
The Walker Press, P.O. Box 141,
Wolfe Island, Ontario

Typesetting by Hanson & Edgar Ltd.
Printing by Brown and Martin, Kingston, Ontario

ISBN for both volumes of this set: 0-9690514-0-9
ISBN for this volume: 0-9690514-1-7

PREFACE OF THE AUTHOR

More than a quarter of a century has passed since my first scientific work dealing with the history of cartography appeared [Bagrow(1912a)]. Since then, every minute of my leisure has been devoted to the study of early maps. The Caspian study was followed by one of the Black Sea. Availing myself of an exhibition on the "Russian Riviera", organized at St. Petersburg in 1913, I arranged there an exhibition of maps illustrating the development of the cartographic portrayal of the Black Sea and printed ten copies of an atlas of these early maps [Bagrow(1914a)]. In 1914, I was entrusted with writing an essay on the history of maps of Asiatic Russia for a large publication being prepared by the Migration Office [1914c].

My subsequent emigration abroad led my interests somewhat away from the study of Russian cartography. I thought I should profit by the opportunity to gain knowledge on the cartography of other peoples and study the maps available in Western Europe. However, I never completely dropped the subject of my main interest, but made every effort to discover authentic Russian maps in European libraries and archives and to study the collected maps relating to Russia. In addition, I rarely missed an opportunity to acquire such maps for my own collection.

The dearth of materials for the study of Russian cartography compelled me to turn my attention to European maps. The result of this inquiry was presented in several of my works [Bagrow (1928), (1930), (1945)] and in many volumes of *Imago Mundi*. My continued studies of the history of the cartography of Russia found expression in a series of articles and the publication of the first volume of the series *Anecdota Cartographica* [Bagrow(1935)].

Simultaneously I collected materials for the compilation of a fundamental work on the cartographic history of Russia, which I intended to elaborate and publish after my return home. There are still many questions to which very little attention has been given in the Russian literature. The initial cartographic work of the Senate has not been sufficiently studied and no information is available on the activity of the War Department, the Mining School and other similar institutions of the eighteenth century. (Published materials throwing light on the role of the Academy of Sciences are more abundant.) For these reasons I put off the publication of the present book, awaiting an opportunity for completing it through studies of the source materials extant in Russian libraries and archives. Time is passing, however, and the chances of returning "home" and resuming one's work there do not seem to be increasing. And if this appears at last to be possible, it may not be too late — one will be like the squirrel of Krÿlov's fable with a pile of nuts and no teeth to crack them.

Therefore, I have decided to bring into order the collected materials, elaborate them and, if possible, get them published. As yet there is no exhaustive work in the history of Russia's cartography, either in Russia or abroad, so I hope that my book, even in its present state of imperfection, may be of some use to students of cartography and may also serve as a point of departure in the compilation of a more complete work.

The plan of my work is the following:

Introduction — a brief essay on the ancient Russians, their awareness of geography, and their ineptitude in graphic expression.

Part I. — the history of ancient and medieval cartography having any relation to the territory of Russia. This is the epoch of manuscript maps by European and Muslim cartographers prior to the invention of the printing-press, i.e. up to and including the 15th century. (An introduction to the history of the cartography of Russia.)

Part II. — works of West-European and Russian cartographers up to the close of the 18th century when Western Enrope had come to rely exclusively upon Russian materials for the compilation of maps of the Russian territories. The end of the 18th century is not an arbitrary boundary as 1800 in Russia saw the organization by Pavel I of the Map Department (*Depot kart*) where all map production was to be centralized. As for the modern history of cartography, I am unable and do not want to describe it — I leave this task to some other scholar.

Part III. — an appendix to that half of Part II which deals purely with Russian cartography. Here I give: 1) an essay based upon a chronological index of maps printed in Russia up to 1800, and 2) an essay based upon a chronological index of Russian surveyors, cartographers, engravers, etc. concerned with the production of Russian maps up to 1800. Naturally, I do not pretend that my register is complete — it is only an essay. The compilation of an exhaustive index would require the collaboration of several scholars and much time and labor.

Throughout my book I am guided by the principle of giving direction to the future researcher, indicating the most important sources relating to the questions and maps discussed. But I refuse to give precise references supporting each of my conclusions or deductions, as is frequently done, because I find it sufficient to give general indications to the pertinent literature. For the young student, who has just started his investigation of a certain period, it would be necessary to read entirely the special literature I indicate. But for a more advanced scholar requiring a reference or a confirmation of his proper inferences [sic], it should be sufficient to cite the text given in my book. This method of referencing is adhered to throughout the first part and partly in the second part of the book, at least in the chapters dealing with West-European maps. But in dealing with purely Russian cartography, which I had studied from original sources, I indicate simultaneously the source of my information. This is not done in order to attach more importance to my materials, but in order to give the researcher the opportunity of studying them himself and perhaps of discovering new and valuable implications which I may have overlooked or not have found.

There is one more difference between the first and second part of this book. In the first part, in examining one or another map or group of maps, I also deal at length with their historical and geographical setting, whereas in the second part I deal only with the maps proper. These latter are, for the most part, printed European maps which have been dealt with before by other authors.

I often used to discuss my work with my friend Dimitry Rudnev. Together we built many castles in the air, but some of our plans also came true — we realized the organization of the Geographical Bureau and the Geographical Institute (the first institution of this kind in the world), which existed independently only ten years and was then incorporated with the University of Leningrad as the Faculty of Geography. There I had planned to open special courses for the study of the history of geodesy and the history of cartography, but this remained unrealized. The latter appears now in the form of this book. But my friend did not live to see it, and I dedicate it to his memory.

Leo Bagrow.

PREFACE OF THE EDITOR

In November, 1964, I received from Dr. Ir. C. Koeman some thousand pages of translated manuscript text by the late Leo Bagrow. I have discovered that it was composed of a number of elements:

1) large sections of Bagrow's history of cartography;
2) large sections of Bagrow's 1945 article on Ptolemy;
3) portions of several other articles which have appeared in *Imago Mundi*, notably those in volumes XI, XIII and XVI; and,
4) a manuscript concerned directly with the history of Russian cartography.

The text which I received was an English translation of a manuscript in Russian in Bagrow's hand; the original is in the possession of his widow in Stockholm. Whether or not it was the original source of all the above-mentioned works is uncertain, but because of its complexity it has been necessary to spend considerable time evaluating it in light of Bagrow's previously published materials; it was important to avoid unnecessary duplication, while at the same time retaining sufficient material to give this work comprehension and cohesion.

Verifying the authenticity of such a large manuscript has necessarily taken a long time. For example, many of the references scattered throughout the manuscript were in a highly abbreviated form — doubtless some shorthand forms familiar to Bagrow, but unfortunately not always clear to the editor or to numerous librarians. Also, despite the excellent work of the two translators, Fru V. Busch and Mr. Vladimir Kreicberg, many correctly rendered sections were less than lucid. Therefore, many of Bagrow's "steps" were retraced in an effort to discover the point of his argument. Undoubtedly the transcription of the manuscript into typed form introduced an additional number of transpositions and errors. Thus a considerable number of years has been spent simply in trying to produce a correct, authentic manuscript.

The next problem was how to best cut the verified manuscript and still to retain Bagrow's scholarly input while, at the same time, producing a unified, comprehensive whole. The manuscript divided itself logically into two sections — one on European mapping of Russia, and the other largely on Russian efforts at mapping their own country. Large portions of the material on European mapping had already been published, although in some cases in languages other than English. Thus much of it might have been removed. However, in the latter Russian section, Bagrow frequently referred to maps or to persons discussed in the former in giving the background to the making of a map. For this reason, it seemed impossible to drop the first section completely, but better to revise it, taking care to keep the focus on the changing image of Russia in the western cartographic picture. This was made easier by the decision to publish Bagrow's manuscript in two volumes rather than in one as we had originally envisioned. Thus, essentially, the first section appears here as Volume I — A History of the Cartography of Russia up to 1600 — and the second section as Volume 2 — A History of Russian Cartography up to 1800.

Even with the freedom of two volumes, it remained necessary to distill the verified manuscript down to manageable proportions. Several devices were utilized to accomplish this. First, entries in the bibliography were organized so that the date of a work immediately followed the author's name; this made it possible to adapt a short-form for use within the text, thereby eliminating a footnote where only a specific reference was given. Thus [(Bagrow(1945)] refers to Bagrow's article on Ptolemy from *Geografiska Annaler*. If a specific page was referred to it might take the form [(Bagrow(1945)377]; if Bagrow's name was a part of the sentence it would be indicated . . . Bagrow[(1945)377] . . .

While this form of citation is found more often in scientific writing than in historical literature, I felt that its use would allow me to present more of Bagrow's text, despite possible undesirable effects it might have on some of my readers. As a reader, I like to know to whom the author is referring without having my train of thought severely interrupted by having to search the bottom of the page or to leaf to the end of the chapter for the specific footnote. Thus I have put the small, single credits within the running text and removed those lengthy, fact-filled asides to the end of the sections where the more interested reader may look at his leisure.

A second shorthand notation was developed in the footnotes for citing reproductions of the maps discussed. When reading articles on historical maps, I am struck by the number of authors who refer to the size of reproductions in subjective terms — "slightly" or "greatly" reduced. So that our readers will know more precisely what the size relationship is between the original and its reproduction, I have given the size of the original in centimetres (the horizontal dimension first then the vertical), such as (47x35); for a circular map, (27 dia.) means that it is 27 centimetres in diameter. The relationship of the original to the particular reproduction is given as a ratio within the reference to the location of the reproduction. For example, reproductions of Mercator's map "Rvssia cum confinijs" (47x35) can be found in Kordt (1899) T.XXIV(1.1), i.e. as Table 24 at the same scale as the original; and in Bagrow (1917) 35 (3:1), i.e. on page 35 at one third the size of the original. Such extended series of numbers may at first startle the reader, but they soon become easy to decipher.

The map dimension that is missing is, of course, the scale. However, I have purposely left it out for a number of interrelated reasons. First, from my experience in teaching cartography, I find that the concept of map scale and the whole study of map projections are among the most difficult concepts to get across. In addition, I feel that the appearance of simple graphic scales on our contemporary small scale maps is one of the greatest oversimplifications perpetrated by cartographers. Thus, I am reluctant to apply such a descriptive dimension to early maps, particularly to those of large sections of the globe where there exists a large amount, and frequently an unknown amount, of scale variation. I suspect, though I have no proof, that early makers of small scale maps did not have as great a concern as we in the variation of scale error across their maps. Thus I feel that some indication of the size of a reproduction relative to the original document might be more meaningful and useful to students of historical cartography, particularly when their research (including calculations of scale and distance) might necessarily be conducted with a reproduction rather than the original.

Selecting illustrations for a volume such as this is always a problem. Given the nature of early maps, it is probable that their contents in terms of names and represented features is of greater significance than the finer detail and the graphic design, although the later in certainly of great interest. With this in mind, I have tried to select maps with legibility foremost in mind so that the reader can better follow the discussions or can make his own observations and analyses. For many of the world maps, this was made possible simply by enlarging the small area covering the Russian lands. For other maps, I have reproduced handmade rather than photographic copies as in the case of Figures 4 & 8. As an aid to describing the developing image of Russia, I have included a series of simplified sketches of a number of the maps, showing the general configuration of the five major rivers of European Russia, re-oriented with the north at the top, and reduced to a common size.

A word should be said about the transliteration system that was used. Choosing a transliteration system is about as delicate a job as selecting a wife for your best friend. No matter who (or which one in our example) you choose, not everyone will be happy. I find transliteration systems are, surprisingly, one of the more emotional topics among those studying in the Russo-Soviet area; everyone seems to have his own private version of one of the several well recognized systems. True to this quirk of the profession, I am using essentially the system of the United States Board of Geographic names with these additions:

1) "ẏ" (i.e. the letter y with a dot immediately above it) to differentiate " ы " (*yerry*) from " й " (*ee kratkoye*) as represented by "y".

2) "ė" (i.e. the letter e with a dot immediately above it) to differentiate " э " (*e Oborotnoye*) from " e " represented by "e".

Students of the Russian language and scholars knowledgeable therein will recognize this as somewhat unnecessary; however, for the benefit of those not so well versed, I have made these additions. They are especially useful in searching out some of the more obscure place names, the spellings of which may not always be consistent with other Russian words. In the preface to Volume 2, I have elaborated on this and other related problems.

The need to transliterate obscure place-names, such as those for villages and small rivers, is, I believe, self-evident. The insoluble question is of course at what point, or more correctly where, does one stop and adopt Anglicized forms. Since this volume will likely find its way to non-English speaking countries, it seemed most logical to Anglicize as few place-names as possible, but to try to use names of local usage, particularly when referring to contemporary place names. Thus "Warszawie" is used rather than "Warsaw" or "Varshava"; "Roma" rather than "Rome" or "Rim"; etc. "Rome" is used, however, in referring to the Mediterranean empire of classical times. Where cardinal directions are apart of the name, I have used the Russian form, e.g. Severnaya Dvina [the Northern Dvina] or The Yuzhnẏy Bug [the South Bug]. The only consistent exception that I have made is in the names of large bodies of water, particularly oceans and large seas bordering on more than one country. Thus I refer to the Black Sea rather than to the Chernoye More; but on the other hand, I generally refer to the Karkinitskiy Zaliv rather than the Karkinitis Bay.

Finally, I should say a word about the text itself. I have tried throughout to retain Bagrow's point of view and opinions and to clarify, as best I could, what I believe these to be. However, in a number of places this was not easy to do, because there has been subsequent research which throws additional or even contradictory light on Bagrow's position. Rather than attempt to intercede in these matters, I have tried to point out to the reader the existence of this research so that he has before him a fairly complete bibliography on the subject under discussion. Incidentally, Bagrow's original manuscript contained frequent asides or declarations written in the first person plural. I have not systematically eliminated nor re-written these, but rather have accepted them as a peculiarity of his writing style.

Unfortunately, Leo Bagrow is not available to assist in the final preparation of the volumes that will bear his name; as a result, his unsolicited student-editor has had to rely on the posthumus "instructions" and the guidance that working with the manuscript has furnished. I am comforted that Bagrow's reputation is secure despite my efforts here, although one hopes that he would have approved of the form and content of these two volumes. In any case, the responsibility for any shortcomings must lie with the editor.

Henry W. Castner,
Kingston, Ontario,
May, 1970.

System of Transliteration

Alphabet	Transliteration	Alphabet	Transliteration
А	a	Р	r
Б	b	С	s
В	v	Т	t
Г	g	У	u
Д	d	Ф	f
Е	e, ye[1]	Х	kh
Ё	yo	Ц	ts
Ж	zh	Ч	ch
З	z	Ш	sh
И	i	Щ	shch
Й	y	Ъ	″[2]
К	k	Ы	ẏ
Л	l	Ь	′
М	m	Э	ė
Н	n	Ю	yu
О	o	Я	ya
П	p		

1. "Ye" initially in a word, after vowels, and after ь .
2. Generally omitted, particularly at the end of words.

TABLE OF CONTENTS

LIST OF FIGURES

LIST OF TABLES

ACKNOWLEDGEMENTS

The editor wishes to thank the many persons who have assisted, over the years, in making possible this volume. Some were helpful in deciphering Bagrow's highly abbreviated citations; or assisted in clarifying some confusing historical points; or searched out some obscure map or academic work, seemingly known only to Bagrow.

In particular, I would like to thank the staff of the Douglas Library of Queen's University, who performed many of the above services and also assisted in securing many materials pertinent to this volume. As to the production of the manuscript itself, I wish to thank Messrs. Peter Pathak and Thomas Fowler, who worked on the bibliography; Ross Hough who prepared the sketches; and Mrs. Audrey Douglas, who typed the manuscript. Special thanks go to my friend Mrs. Helen Allan, who proof-read the manuscript, made many valuable editorial suggestions, and compiled the index. I also wish to express my appreciation to Queen's University, which has generously made available travel funds to allow me to visit distant libraries and archives, both in North America and in Europe.

Finally, to my wife Claire, my gratitude for her patience, assistance and encouragement throughout the years we have been working with the manuscript.

Henry W. Castner

PART I: IMAGE OF RUSSIA IN ANCIENT TIMES

Chapter 1:

Of Scythia and Sarmatia

Introduction

The vast plain of European Russia is the source of a number of great rivers which have been important transportation arteries back into the past. None of these great rivers, however, appears to have been a cultural hearth as were the Nile, the Tigris and the Indus. As a result, the people who first inhabited these areas, and indeed many who followed, left us few records or monuments. All that survived them is either quite alien, or borrowed, or from later centuries. As a result, we must look elsewhere for our first geographic information on the Russian lands, i.e. those areas which were later to become part of Russia.

One of the areas of earliest Western contact with peoples of the Russian lands was that along the coasts of the Black and Caspian Seas. Surviving *peripli*, or sailing directions, show continuing contact from the 4th century B.C. (that of Scylax Caryandensis (Figure 1) for the western part of the Black Sea up to the Straits of Kerch', and that of Patroclus for the Caspian Sea) and suggest much earlier intercourse between Western traders and indigenous populations. The earliest *peripli*, actually, are not only guides to navigation, but reports of voyages as well. They contain descriptions of the coastal waters, harbours, etc., and often information on the countries themselves. But as it was important to keep the navigational information concise and up-to-date, superfluous descriptive information in later *peripli* was kept to a minimum or omitted.

Herodotus

For the earliest information on the interior of the Russian lands, we must consult some of the early writers of antiquity who reported contemporary happenings as well as past events and legends. One such writer is the Greek historian Herodotus (484-425 B.C.). His history includes an account of the Egyptian campaign in Scythia in the days of Sesostris, about 1400 B.C. Sesostris, who is known for his extensive campaigns in Asia, erected pillars in Scythia in commemoration of this campaign and allegedly compiled maps of all the countries which he conquered! This report, however, is viewed with some skepticism by the author [Bagrow(1964)32].

As to the geography of Scythia, Herodotus gives detailed and valuable information in his account of Darius' campaign in Scythia, about 519 B.C. [Book IV, Chapter 1-82]. Herodotus had himself travelled to Scythia and there tried to collect available material concerning it. In general he states that the country has no marvels except its rivers, which are larger and more numerous than those of any other land. "These, and the vastness of the great plain, are worthy of note. . . "[Book IV, Chapter 82]. He mentions eight of the most famous rivers; the Ister (the Danube); the Tyras (the Dnestr); the Hypanis (the Yuzhnyy Bug); the Borysthenes (the Dnepr); the Panticapes (probably the Ingulets); the Hypacyris (presumably the Kalanchak); the Gerrhus (whose identity has not yet been established); and finally, the Tanais (the Don) [Book IV, Chapters 47-57].

The Ister, which has five mouths, is the mightiest of all these rivers for it never varies in height, but continues at the same level summer and winter. Starting from the west, it is the first of the Scythian rivers. The next, the Tyras, rises from a great lake and runs a southerly course to the sea. The third river is the Hypanis, which rises in another large lake and which is known in its upper course for the sweetness and purity of its water.

The fourth river, the Borysthenes, is, next to the Ister, the greatest of them all; and, in Herodotus' judgment, is the most productive river, not merely in Scythia but in the whole world, excepting only the Nile. Its course is known far inland to a place named

Gerrhus — some forty days' voyage from the sea. Its direction is from north to south. Not long before it reaches the sea, the Borysthenes is joined by the Hypanis. Next in succession is the fifth river, the Panticapes, which rises from a lake, flows from north to south, and empties into the Borysthenes. Obviously, if this is the Ingulets, Herodotus' succession is reversed here. The sixth stream the Hypacyris, runs directly through the "middle of the Nomadic Scythians".

The seventh river, the Gerrhus, is referred to above in the upper reaches of the Borysthenes. The eighth river is the Tanais. Its source is far up country in a lake of vast size, and it empties into another still larger lake, the Palus Maeotis (Sea of Azov).

With the exception of the Danube, only the lower courses of these rivers were known to Herodotus, although he says they are navigable some distance from the sea. [Book IV, Chapter 47]. Settlements upstream were not only unknown to him but he even states with assurance that there were none [Book IV, Chapter 46]. Thus he does not hesitate to let the Scythian tzar, Idanthyrsus, utter the words "We Scythians have neither towns nor cultivated lands. . ." [Book IV, Chapter 127].

Herodotus also had knowledge about the Caspian Sea. Contrary to the Ionian scholars who considered the Caspian to be one of four gulfs of the encircling world ocean, Herodotus states that it is a sea having no connection with any other, lying by itself, which is in length fifteen days' voyage with a rowboat and, at the broadest part, eight days' voyage in breadth. Along its western shore runs the chain of the Caucasus, the most extensive and loftiest of all mountain ranges. To the east, the Caspian is followed "by a vast plain, stretching out interminably before the eye" [Book I, Chapters 203-204]. Finally, Herodotus gives a great deal of ethnographic information on the country, such as tribal names, places of their occupation, and some information on their activities.

Strabo

Another Greek writer was Strabo (63 B.C.-26 A.D.) who wrote a lengthy treatise called the *Geography*. In general, he gives much the same picture of the Russian lands as does Herodotus although he gives somewhat more detail to the areas east of the Euxine (Black Sea); there are, however, some significant exceptions.

Of the major rivers flowing into the north coast of the Black Sea, he makes the mistake of placing the Hypanis to the east of the Borysthenes [Book VII, Chapter III, Part 17]. However, he correctly places Olbia some two hundred stadia upstream on the

Borysthenes. As to the Tanais, he states that its sources are unkown [XI, II, 2]. Finally, he states that the Caspian Sea, also called the Hyrcanian, "is the gulf which extends from the ocean toward the south; it is rather narrow at its entrance, but it widens out as it advances inland,. . .where its width is approximately five thousand stadia" [XI,VI,2].

As for cartographic records, the Greeks did not produce any detailed maps embracing the then known world, or even large portions of it. Thus we can gain no further insight here into their knowledge of Russian lands. There are several treatises on the theoretical aspects of map construction by Marinus of Tyre. Marinus' work has not reached us but we know of it from a work by Claudius Ptolemy, his contemporary at Alexandria and a famous astronomer and mathematician. Ptolemy, in his polemical work the *Geographia*, analyses what he believes to be defects in the theory put forth by Marinus, and arrives at the conclusion [Book I, Chapter 18] that Marinus' instructions cannot possibly be used for constructing a map. Ptolemy in fact claims that many have tried unsuccessfully to prepare a map after his instructions.

Ptolemy

As for Ptolemy, he is of greater importance to our story, and indeed to the history of cartography, because some of his work has survived. Specifically, a number of manuscript copies of the above-mentioned *Georgraphia* have come down to us, but from the last centuries of the Byzantine Empire - over a millennium after Ptolemy's lifetime. An apparent void in knowledge of Ptolemy and this work during this thousand year period has led scholars to examine the question of the origin of the various parts of these manuscripts. To recapitulate all of the various arguments which have been set forth is beyond the scope of these pages; [2] instead we can only refer to several of the conclusions, particularly those held by the author. Briefly, let us examine this question in greater detail before proceeding to analyse the data attributed to Ptolemy himself.

As we stated, our knowledge of Ptolemy's *Geographia* comes not from the 2nd century, but primarily from manuscripts which came to light in 13th-14th century Byzantium. Some of these are provided with maps, others are not. Even those containing maps are not all alike: two different versions are known — Version A, comprising 27 large maps which are collected as a part of Book VIII, and Version B, comprising 64 smaller maps scattered in the text. Altogether 52 manuscrips of Ptolemy's *Geographia*, both complete and incomplete, are known to us. Maps are found in 11 manuscripts of Version A and in 5 manuscripts of Version B.

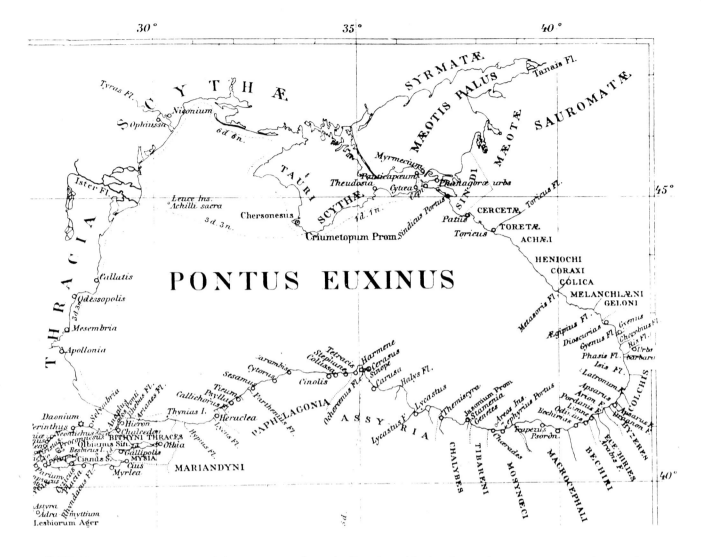

FIGURE 1. A reconstruction of the text names from the Periplus of Scylax Caryandensis superimposed upon the modern outline of the Black Sea. After C. Müller(1855) from Nordenskiöld(1897).

Differences between the information which is presented in the maps and that which is found in various parts of the textual materials (in these manuscripts) have led researchers[3] to conclude that much of the data could not have been given by Ptolemy, but only by later authors. This led to further evaluations of the maps and the component parts of *The Geographia* manuscripts and to attempts to retrace possible routes which Ptolemy's 2nd century work might have taken to reach 13th century Byzantium. These attempts brought to light the fact that many ancient writers during this thousand years were not familiar with either Ptolemy himself, or his maps. For example, Pappus, an Alexandrian who presumably lived at the time of Diocletian (280-305), is credited with a revision of Ptolemy by the anonymous author of an Armenian Geography. The anonymous author, who was most likely Anania Shirakazi (7th C.), states that he took excerpts from Pappus Alexandrinus who had derived and abbreviated Ptolemy's work

[Bagrow(1945)325]. Sometime during the 5th century A.D., another author, Stephanus Byzantius, compiled a lexicon of peoples. Unfortunately, his work has reached us in badly multilated condition. But in the portions which have survived there are numerous references to various authors — Strabo, Marcian, Hekataeus, Hellanikos — but no mention is made of Ptolemy. Marcian (about 400 A.D.) also refers to Ptolemy in his *Periplus* without, however, mentioning Ptolemy's maps. The author suggests [(1945) 328] that both Marcian and Ptolemy had availed themselves of some other periplus. These are apparently the principal Greek derivatives known during the period immediately following Ptolemy. In succeeding centuries, there are a number of Syrian and Arabic translations of the *Geographia*, (the first Syrian translation in 555 A.D.) but of course these would neither be known nor available in the West. Apparently Ptolemy's reputation in the Moslem world rested on other mathematical and astronomical works, rather than on the *Geographia*.

Even the Metropolitan Eustaph of Thessalonica, writing a detailed commentary to Dionisius in the second half of the 12th Century, mentions Ptolemy only on one occasion; in referring to the Caspian as an enclosed basin, while omitting all the more particular information provided by the *Geographia*. All this leads us to assume that Ptolemy's *Geographia*, in the state in which it later appeared in Byzantium, was not known in the centuries immediately following the age of Ptolemy and that at a date later than has hitherto been belived, was joined together from separate parts to form the *Geographia*.

We have mentioned all this because Ptolemy is considered to be the initiator of the cartography of Russia. His work has hitherto been ascribed to the middle of the 2nd century A.D. and our conception of the Russian lands of that day is formed from it. However, the greater part of his geographical material is of a later date than the fundamental parts of Ptolemy's work, i.e. Book I, which is primarily concerned with theoretical matters of geography and cartography, and the list of the most important towns included in Book VIII. It is therefore necessary to consider separately these two fundamental parts from those which were probably included by a later author(s) or compiler(s), namely Books II to VII.

There is information relating to the territory of present-day Russia in both of these time divisions. The information contained in Book VIII, Chapters 10 (the 8th map of Europe) and 18 (the 2nd map of Asia) can undoubtedly be ascribed to Ptolemy. Specifically, we are referring to the text on the reverse of these maps and not to the maps themselves. This seems to constitute the sum of the exact knowledge which Ptolemy utilized. More exhaustive information on Scythia was certainly available at the beginning of the 2nd century A.D., but much of it was descriptive and therefore of little use to Ptolemy in defining geographical points. Within Books II to VII, Book III, Chapter 5 (European Sarmatia) and Book V, Chapter 8 (Asiatic Sarmatia) refer to Russian lands. [4] While the dating of the various contributions to the *Geographia* is still uncertain, we must nevertheless bear in mind that in dealing with the *Geographia*, we are not dealing exclusively with 2nd century A.D. materials, but with materials from many different periods.

Sarmatia

Concerning the information on Sarmatia given in Book VIII, i.e. that which is attributed to Ptolemy, the following is taken from Latýshev's translation [(1948)II,231-257].

Book VIII, Chapter 10, the 8th map of Europe:

"The 8th map of Europe comprises European Sarmatia and the Tauric Chersonese. The parallel extending through its centre stands in relation to the meridian as 11 to 20.

In the east, this map is bounded by the Cimmerian Bosporus, Lake Meotese and the river Tanaid opposite Asiatic Sarmatia; in the south — by the Pontus Sea, a part of Missia, Dacia and the region of the Yazigue immigrants; in the west — by the so-called Sarmatian Mountains, Germany, and the river Vistula; in the north by the Venetian Gulf of the Sarmatian Ocean and yet unkown land.

Of the most important towns of Sarmatia, Gamirakha's longest day is 16 equinoctial hours and its distance from Alexandria [to the west] is 1 /15 equinoctial hour.

Navar's longest day is 16 hours, 15 minutes and its distance from Alexandria [to the west] is 1 /8 hour.

Olvia's or Borisphenida's, longest day is 16 hours, 5 minutes and its distance from Alexandria [to the west] is 1 /5 hour.

Of the towns of the Tauric Chersonese, Theodosia's longest day is 15 hours, 15 minutes and its distance from Alexandria to the east is 1 /5 hour.

The longest day of Pantikapea is 15 hours, 55 minutes and its distance from Alexandria to the east is 1 /4 hour."

Book VIII, Chapter 8, the 2nd map of Asia:

Asia, map 2 comprises Sarmatia situated in Asia. The parallel passing through its centre stands in relation to the meridian as 7 to 12.

In the east, it is bounded by Scythia and a part of the Caspian Sea: in the south - by part of the Euxine Pontus, Colchis, Iberia and Albany; in the west - by European Sarmatia, Lake Meotese and the Cimmerian Bosporus; in the north - by unknown land.

Of the known Sarmatian towns, Ermonassa's longest day is 15 hours, 50 minutes and its distance from Alexandria to the east is 1 /3 equinoctial hour.

Inanfia's longest day is 15 hours, 50 minutes, and its distance from Alexandria to the east is nearly 1 /2 hour.

Tanaid's longest day is 17 hours, 10 minutes and its distance from Alexandria to the east is 1 /26 hour.

Tiramba's longest day is 16 hours, 12 minutes and its distance from Alexandria to the east is 1 /10 hour.

Navarida's [5] longest day is 17 hours, 15 minutes and its distance from Alexandria to the east is 1 /3 hour.

FIGURE 2.   Part of the world map from the Roma edition of Ptolemy's *Geographia* published in 1478. Slightly enlarged (5:7).

The hour co-ordinates given by Ptolemy do not always conform with those given in Books III and V, although with the exception of the longitudes of the last four points in Asiatic Sarmatia, there is general agreement between them (Table I). However, one would not expect so many divergencies from the hand of a single author, much less of one of the stature of Ptolemy. In addition, these few points are hardly sufficient to structure the maps which we find attached to the various manuscripts of the *Geographia*. A close check of the position of these points above, which are shown on the maps of Sarmatia, reveals that the information in Books III and V was used in making the maps. Since this information is from a later date, they will be described later on. It might be helpful, however, to make an exception here with the general map on one sheet (Figure 2) for it probably does represent

materials of the 2nd-3rd centuries A.D., [6] and as such is one of the earliest portrayals of the future territory of Russia, even though we recognize that its production took place many hundreds of years later.

The general map on one sheet is found, as a rule, at the end of Book VII and is preceded by: three chapters giving general instructions for preparing maps; a general description of the known world at that time with the three interior seas — the Mediterranean, Caspian and Indian Ocean with their bays and islands; and instructions for drawing a sphere and for representing the world on a plane surface. On some of these maps, and also in some of the MSS without maps, there is an inscription stating that according to the materials of the eight geographical books of Claudius Ptolemy, a portrayal of the whole world was drawn by "Agathos Daimon of Alexandria,

| | | LONGITUDE | | | | LATITUDE | | |
| | | Ptolemy Book VIII | Books III & V | | | Ptolemy Book VIII | Books III & V | |
		Hours	Degrees			Hours	Degrees	
European Sarmatia	Tamyrica	1/15 h to the W	59°00′	59°20′		16 h	48°30′	48°30′
	Naubarum	1/8 h to the W	58°10′	58°30′		16 h 15m	50°10′	50°00′
	Olbia	1/5 h to the W	57°00′	57°00′		16 h 5m	49°00′	49°00′
	Theodosia	1/5 h to the E	63°00′	63°00′		15 h 50m	47°30′	47°20′
	Pantikapea	1/4 h to the E	63°45′	64°00′		15 h 55m	47°50′	47°55′
Sarmatia in Asia	Hermonasa	1/3 h to the E	65°00′	65°00′		15 h 50m	47°30′	47°30′
	Oenathia	1/2 h to the E	67°30′	69°40′		15 h 50m	47°30′	47°15′
	Tanais	1/26 h to the E	60°35′	67°00′		17 h 10m	54°50′	54°20′
	Tyramba	1/10 h to the E	58°30′	69°40′		16 h 12m	50°00′	49°50′
	Naubaxis	1/3 h to the E	65°00′	70°00′		17 h 15m	55°10′	55°00′

TABLE I

The table presents the hour co-ordinates of the points transferred into co-ordinates of degrees as derived from Book VIII (Ptolemy) and Books III and V respectively.

mechanikos'' (engineer or surveyor). [7] The previous three chapters are also attributed by many scholars to this Agathodaemon. His identity and lifetime are, however, unknown. Some scholars assume him to have been a contemporary of Ptolemy, who entrusted him with retracing a map of his [Ptolemy's] own; others belive him to have lived in the 5th century. However, we may just as well assume that he lived in the 9th or 10th century, when all the 8 Books of the *Geographia* were likely joined together into one work. Agathodaemon may have collaborated in this compilative work and offered to complete it with chapters and maps of his own authorship. We know nothing for certain, but we can state that Agathodaemon did not introduce any new material into his map and thus the data he used may be ascribed without hesitation to the 2nd-3rd centuries A.D.

As for the area of our present interest, his map provides very little information. We should keep in mind, however, that it is one of the earliest portrayals of the future territory of Russia. Notwithstanding, the hydrographic net it presents was generally accepted as a basis for the construction of many later maps. European and Asiatic Sarmatia has three rivers — the Borysthenes, the Tanais and the Rha (Volga). The two last-mentioned approach one another in their middle course and then draw apart again. The Rha is formed by the confluence of two rivers flowing from mountains in the northeast and northwest respectively. The Black Sea, the Sea of Azov, and the Caspian Sea are shown. Also indicated are the Tavrica Chersonese and, between the Black and Caspian Seas, Colchis, Iberia and Albany successively. This is all. There are no other details or place-names. In the Latin MSS. a few more rivers, discharging into the Baltic and Azov Seas, have been added, but these MSS. are, of course, of a still later time.

Chapter 2:

Mediterranean Concepts

From Alexandria, we should be able to trace Ptolemy's influence in three directions: to Rome; to Constantinople, i.e. the Eastern Roman Empire; and to the Arab Empire, which was soon to occupy much of the Mediterranean lands once held by these other two powers (reaching Spain in 711). However, this is not easily done. But let us briefly consider these directions.

Rome

The rise of Rome was initially accompanied by the acquisition of much of the territory of the old Greek empire, but little of its culture. While the Romans' basic cosmographical concept was essentially the same as the Greeks - a flat disc surrounded by the ocean - they took little interest in theoretical deliberations concerning the overall shape of the world or in the best means of representing it graphically. In Rome, more practical problems were considered: the distances between points were measured for such purposes as laying out roads or surveying land.

For example, as a result of road surveys carried out during the reign of Emperor Augustus, a map of the known world was presumably produced by Marcus Vipsanius Agrippa (63-12 B.C.). While a number of copies of the map were made, not a single one survives. We do have indirect knowledge of its contents from such writers as Pliny[8], who states, for example: "Agrippa considers the whole of this region [Dacia and Sarmatia], from the Ister to the ocean, to be 2100 miles in length, and 4400 miles in breadth to the river Vistula in the deserts of Sarmatia" [Book IV, Chapter 25]. "The length of Sarmatia, Scythia, and Taurica, and of the whole of the region which extends from the river Borysthenes is, according to Agrippa, 980 miles, and its breadth 717". Pliny qualifies these statements by adding: "I am of the opinion, however, that in this part of the earth all estimates of measurement are exceedingly doubtful" [IV,26]. Pliny also gives considerable attention to the Black and Caspian

Seas and the territories adjacent to them. But since he is largely indebted to Greek writers for his information, there is little that is significantly different from that given by Herodotus. [9]

Tabula Peutingeriana

Another itinerary map was the so-called Tabula Peutingeriana. It is not a document of the 3rd century although its origin has been traced to about A.D. 250 when it was copied from a larger original of the 1st century A.D. Additions were made in about 350 (the coastline was improved and some islands were added), at the turn of the 5th-6th century (the World Ocean), and even into the 8th-9th century (a few insignificant local corrections). However, in general, its form was more or less fixed around 500 A.D. In this state it was discovered by Conrad Celtes, a humanist of Wien and Librarian to Maximilian I. From Celtes it passed to the well-known collector of antiques Conrad Peutinger, whose name it bears.

Typically, this map has no projection[10] so that measurements of distance upon it is not always successful - for this we have figures written on the map by the map's author between points (Figure 3). However, for the territory of our interest, i.e. European and Asiatic Sarmatia, there are no figures because there were no roads north of the Black Sea from the estuary of the Danube to "Trapehunt" (probably Phasis but perhaps Trapezus, the modern Trebizond) on the east coast of the Black Sea near the mouth of the Rioni River. From this latter point roads do continue to the southeast via Transcaucasia to the Caspian and Persia. No roads run northwards beyond the Rioni and Kura Rivers.

As for the geographical appearance of the map, the east-west extension of the land situated north of the "Pontvs Evxinvs" (Black Sea) is incredibly great. The latitudinal extent of the whole or Sarmatia (i.e.,

FIGURE 3.   Constantinople on the road from London to Jerusalem with the Black Sea and Sarmatia to the north; a portion of the highly attenuated Tabula Peutingeriana. Courtesy the British Library Board. Slightly enlarged (6:7).

from the north shore of the Black Sea to the North Ocean) is related to the width of the Black Sea as 1:22; similarly, the latitudinal extent of the "Lacus Meotidis" (Sea of Azov) stands to its own width as 1:12. As a result, positional discrepancies occur such as with the location of "Phaniacorium" on the coast of the Black Sea east of Meotidis at a distance equivalent to the length of Lacus Meotidis itself. (Phanagoria, the ancient Greek colony, is near the present-day Taman' on the Tamanskiy Zaliv (Gulf) opposite the city of Kerch').

Proceeding along the coast of the Black Sea, starting at the mouth of the Danube, we see: the "Agalingus" (the Dnestr); the "Selliani", which joins a river rising in the "[Hip]anis paludis" (the Yuzhnyy Bug); and then the "Nusacus" (the Dnepr) rising in a small lake (the Amadoka?). Four rivers flow into the "Lacus Meotidis": the "Tanais" (the Don) ". . . qui diuidit asiam et europam"; the easternmost of these rivers, presumably the Kuban', crosses a lake. A number of peoples are indicated: the "Roxulani Sarmate", the "Sorices", the "Meotes", the "Aspurgiani", the "alani" and others. Many population centres are shown to the south of the Sea of Azov in the country of "Bosforani". Here we see "Cabacos", "Hermoca", "Nimphi", "Chimmerium", etc. Thus the Tabula Peutingeriana provides little new information relating to the territory of Russia. This we would expect as the Roman Empire did not expand as far as the northern coast of the Black Sea.

Roman Shield

One other relic of the Roman era which deserves attention is the bronze shield of a Roman soldier found in excavations at Dura Europas near the Euphrates. Although this place is known to have been a station of the Roman army, the shield is undoubtedly of Greek origin because fragments of an itinerary drawn on it have Greek inscriptions. Cumont, in his descriptions of the shield, assumes it to be a monument of Roman cartography because 1) it belonged to a Roman soldier, and 2) the map was apparently drawn after records of Roman itineraries.

Portions of the Black Sea can still be distinguished on it as well as the following names: Odes[sos], Bibona, Kallatis, Tomea, Istrospot, Danoubispot, Tura, Borus[en]es, Cherson, Trap..., Arti..., ..an... Here the shield is broken off. Cumont reads two of the latter to be Trapezus and Artaxata. This would mean a sudden leap from the Tauric Peninsula (i.e. Kherson) to Armenia (Trapezus). Uhden's(1932) interpretation seems more reasonable - Trap[ezous], Arda[bda] and [P]an[tikapaion] - i.e. the mountain Trapezus located by Strabo (Book VII,

Chapter 309) between the Chersonese and Theodosia and identified with Chatÿr-Dag by Pallas; the town of Theodosia (Feodosiya);[1] and the town Pantikopea (Kerch').

Given the Romans' practical inclination, it is not difficult to see why Ptolemy's influence upon Roman scholars was apparently slight. For example, the historian Ammianus Marcellinus (c. 380 A.D.) refers once to Ptolemy. However, this reference indicates that he neither knew nor used Ptolemy, although this is a point of some uncertainty [Bagrow(1945)329].

Ptolemy's Influence on the Arabs

As to Ptolemy's influence in the Eastern empire we have already mentioned the works of Pappus, Anania Shirakazi, Stephanus, Agathodaemon, and Marcian of Heraclea. These works suggest Ptolemy's influence was certainly not great, although until more Byzantine records are uncovered and studied this cannot be a final conclusion. Certainly the destruction of the great library at Alexandria, late in the 3rd century A.D., and the occupation by Arabs of former Hellenistic cities around the eastern Mediterranean in the 6th-7th centuries must have restricted European access to and knowledge of Ptolemy's original materials. Cosmos of Alexandria, Indicopleustes (6th C.), could cite familiarly from Ptolemy [Taylor(1957)89], yet Jacob of Edessa (640-708), who recognized the spherical form of the earth and divided as did Ptolemy, the oecumene into 180 degrees of longitude, makes no reference to Ptolemy.

As to the Arabs, very little information has come down to us on the literature and science of the pre-Islamic age. The literary form of the Arabic language first began to develop at the end of the 7th century A.D., when the Arabs began their period of expansion. First, reforms were made in the alphabet, and later Arabic was introduced as an official language in business. While the necessity existed for astronomic information and geographical knowledge (for finding a way to Mecca), the Arabs lacked any such sciences of their own. Thus, it was necessary for Calif al-Mansur (754-775) to have the first astronomical tables translated from Indian tables in Sanscrit. Al-Gazari's translation of 772-773 initiated their own study of astronomy. Not until the reign of Calif Mammun (812-834) was a college opened at Bagdad for translating Greek manuscripts, which were being purchased in Byzantium.

Whether or not any cartographic activity preceded this epic is difficult to establish. Certainly there were contacts made with remote countries and these required travelling guides or itineraries. For example, an embassy travelled to China via Kashgar in

704-715.[12] In any case, no reliable information on maps of the Arabs prior to Mammun has reached us, and we can assume that they began first to appear only after the manuscripts obtained in Byzantium provided the Arabs with geographical material. Buczek[(1963)21] states that there was a widespread tendency in the Arab world of the 9th to the 14th centuries to adapt and develop the Greek heritage in all fields of science, including geography. Thus we can see that in the early Islamic period, the influence of Greek authors, such as Ptolemy, could dominate any Arabic cartographic expression. The extent, however, to which this took place is very difficult to establish. Concerning the region of our interest this is particularly true because we have sufficient knowledge about only one map from this period. This is a map of Meotis from a description of the World (Kitab surat al-ard) by Muhammad ibn Mufa al-Khwarizmi prepared about 820. Actually there is some question whether al-Khwarizmi made any maps at all[13] or whether he merely wrote his books while studying maps made by others.

al-Khwarizmi's Map

As to the map of Meotis, there are mountains in its four corners: in the northwest, near the sea, a nameless mountain-ridge crossed by two rivers "from the marsh to the sea"; in the northeast, the "Iffikas" (Hippici Montes); in the southeast, the "Kauka" mountains (Caucasus); in the southwest, another nameless mountain-ridge. Curiously, the name "Meotis" is lacking, and the only indication given is "al-Batiha", i.e. a marsh. A number of rivers discharge into the "marsh": the Tanais, rising in the north from "Lake Tanis"; from the Iffikas Mountains, the "Marubis" with the town "Savaris" (Navaris), the "burabis" (Rhombits), the "amastas" (Malyi Rombit?), the "atiktos" (Atticitus), and the "tevatani" (Teophanius); from the Caucasus flow two nameless rivers with the town "Medinet" (Termi or Tirambe) between them. Two rivers rising from the "marsh" flow northwestwards to the sea: the westernmost of them is the "Agar" (Agarus), and the other is nameless. Finaly, a river rises from a small lake and flows southwards. This lake is evidently the Cimmerian Bosphorus and the Euxine.

Granted the names are similar to those of Ptolemy's Geographia, but they are also found in the works of other Greek classisists. As for the shape of the "marsh" and the direction of the rivers and mountain-chains, there is absolutely no similarity with Ptolemy's indications. Thus it seems that the Geographia had no direct bearing on the map of the Meotis in al-Khwarizmi's work.[14]

The influence of European sources is seen in a number of imitations of climatic and T-in-O maps. A number of them include information about the territory of Russia. Al-Kharaqi's map (1136) indicates, inter alia, the Khazars in the 6th climate and the Slavonians (Sokalibs). Al-Kazwini (1263) also indicates the Sokalibs, Kipchaks and Rus in the 6th climate and Bulgars in the 7th climate. The Syrian Bar Hebraeus [Miller(1926-1931)1226-1286; Yusuf Kamal (1936)IV, Part I,1096] included in his climatic map a much greater number of names, not only of peoples but also of towns. Indicated in the 6th climate are Alans, Khazars, Kirgise, the Euxine, Slavonians, Kipchaks, bahr Gurgan (the Caspian Sea); indicated in the 7th climate are Bulgars, sekutaje (Scythians), barestani (the Dnepr), and jamma de-warang (the Varangian Sea).

Islamic Atlases

The next period in Arabic cartography is characterized by collections of maps attached to geographical treatises; the number and the content of the maps in various collections are quite similar and they no longer show any traces of European influence. Neither do they reflect any influence of Ptolemy or the maps that later became known as Ptolemy's Geographia. Typically each collection, called an Islamic Atlas or Atlas of Islam, consists of 21 maps: one world map, three sea-charts (Mediterranean, Persian Gulf and the Caspian) and 17 maps of individual Islamic countries. Thus only the world map and the Caspian sea-chart contain information on Russia.[15]

The interrelationship between the world map and the other maps is difficult to establish. However, from the similarity of draftsmanship in the world and other maps, it appears that the world map is compiled from the other maps. Generally, the world is represented as a disc surrounded by the sea, with two large gulfs penetrating the land in the west (the Mediterranean)and in the east (the Persian Gulf with the Red and Arabian Seas off it).[16] In Europe are noted: al lania (the land of Alans), al rus, bulgar, al sakaliba (of Slavonians); in Asia are indicated the Khozar Sea (Caspian) and the river Atib (the Volga) and the Khwarezm Sea (Aral) with the river Geikum (the Amu-Dar'ya), and Al Sarvi (the land of the Golden Throne).

Later revisions of these maps were either simplified or, on the other hand, redrawn in a more complex manner. Typical of the former was the map of the Seven Seas made by al-Biruni (1021). Here a circle encloses a smaller disc indented by five gulfs or seas (one of the gulfs contains two seas - the Mediterranean and the Black Sea). Within the continent is shown: "bahr gorgan" (the Caspian and the adjoining land of the Khozars); Constantinople on the coast of

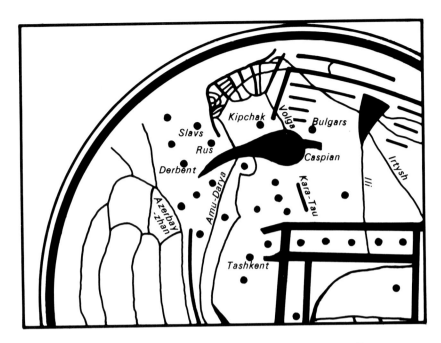

FIGURE 4.   A portion of the Turkish world map of al Kāshgarī redrawn
with transliterated names from Herrmann(1935). Slightly
reduced (7:5).

"Bahr bontus" (the Black Sea); and in the north, "Bahr uarank" (the Varangian Sea) — on its southeast coast live Varangians and on its southwest coast "sakeliba" (Slavonians) and Rus. We also know of a number of versions of a schematic map produced by the above mentioned al-Kazwīnī. The abridged version shows only the Varangian, Euxine, Giurgen (Caspian), and other seas. The completed map indicates, in addition, the peoples: Khozards, Slavonians, Rus, Bulgars, etc.

One other schematic map of this type is the map (Figure 4) of al-Kāshgarī (1074) which comprises extensive parts of Central Asia including China! [7] It was prepared before the Turks had begun their westward expansion, when they still occupied the territory of Central Asia. Besides the names indicated in the Islamic Atlas, we see indicated west of the Caspian, the Pechenegs; the "baskert" (the Bashkirs) far east of the Caspian; and the Kipchags west of the Volga.

Arabic cartography of the third period (the Norman-Arabian period of K. Miller) can be attributed almost entirely to the grandiose work created by Idrisi, and perhaps it would be even more suitable to give it his name. His work sprang from both Arabic and European materials: however, he elaborated and transformed them into a composition all his own. While his material was used later by other cartographers, it is his work that we shall briefly examine.

First let us consider his materials. Russia was more accessible to the Arabs than to any other nation. In their trade and expansion toward Europe, the Arabs met with resistance from Byzantium, Rome and later Venezia. They were free, however, to move northwards along the coast of the Caspian and up the Volga. That they penetrated far into the north is shown by diverse findings which include Arab coins among the Samoyeds and plates being Cufic inscriptions among the Ostiaks. At Murom (on the Oka River) more than 10,000 Arab coins were found; and on the coast of Lake Ladoga one find provided more than two quintals of silver Cufic coins. Thus information on the population of the Volga region and the area west of it began to reach the Muslim world as early as the 7th century. The Khan of Bab al Abdaba, Shakhrian (644), declared that waging war is a customary occupation for him because his neighbours are the Khazars on one side and on the other the Rus, who are the enemies of the whole world and particularly of the Arabs! [8] Hardadbah, the chief postmaster, was familiar with the trading routes of the Rus merchants. The Muslim faith also penetrated the Volga region, and in 921 Calif Muktadir sent an embassy from Bagdad to the newly converted Bulgars. To this embassy was attached Ibn Fadlan, who was charged with recording everything he might hear and see. On their way, the embassy stopped at Ityll (the Tatar name for the Volga is Itil) where they collected information on the Rus, Khazars and Bashkirs. Ibn Fadlan's notes later served as original source material for various geographical treatises. We also know, among other travellers, Adn-Dolaf Misaris ben Mohalhal, who crossed the country of the Pechenegs (943); Massudi, who frequently travelled in the Caucasus and met Rus and Slavonians (described in 947); Haukal also made frequest commercial journeys and appended to his "Book of Routes and States" a few maps of the Islamic Atlas type (in 977). In one of his journeys he met a man named Istahri who said that the Rus consisted of three tribes: the King of one resides in a town named Kuyaba (Kiev), and is closely related to the Bulgars; the second tribe is called Slavia; the third, Artania, whose king resides in Arta. Ibrahim ibn Yakut, a native of north Africa, also travelled widely - presumably as a trader in slaves. He crossed the western part of Europe and came to the Baltic Sea (c. 965). He was especially interested in the western Slavonians. All these travellers provide information of some kind on the Rus and the Slavonians. This information, which was characteristic of its day, found reflection in a whole series of maps during the 9th and 10th centuries, the flowering period of Arabic geography![9]

During this same period, the Norman conquerors began to appear in Western Europe. Eventually, they penetrated the Mediterranean and by the 11th century had settled in southern Italy. The Norman king, Roger II of Sicily (1097-1154), became interested in geography and the development of the geographical sciences. In that day, Palermo was the meeting place for mariners, traders, pilgrims, crusaders, and scholars from many countries, and thus a clearing house for information on distant lands. It was not surprising then that the idea of collecting and recording this information into a book and a map developed there.

Period of Idrisi

A member of Roger's court was the scholar Idrisi. He had been invited there by the king himself and entrusted with the compilation of this book. Idrisi (1099-1164) was well-suited to his task because of his education in Cordoba where he had profited by the geographical knowledge accumulated in Spain, and because of his wide travels - as far north as England

and as far east as Asia Minor. After 15 years work, he finished one book and one map. Then in 1154, the manuscript of another book (in Latin and Arabic), a map on 17 sheets, and a circular general map were completed.[20] Given the great potential of knowledge of the Rssian lands, Idrisi's maps (Figure 5) are somewhat disappointing although their appreciation is necessarily diminished by the difficulty in obtaining precise transcriptions of the toponymy. For example, Table II summarizes some of the contradictions that can arise in reading the Arabic. In addition, Shcheglov(1876) carried out a comparison of the names for Kiev in different Arabic and Persian geographical manuscrips translated by Harkavi and Fren. The name of Kiev varies as follows: Kugaba, Kunaba, Kunaya, Kurbaya, Kerbaya, Karkayana, Kersabe, Karbane, Kubabe, Kubate, Kyuzaba, Kubaze, Kubane, Kibae, Kutate, Kutaze, Kitae, Kuzate, Kuzaya, Kuyabe, Kuyae, Kunane, Kuzase, Kar-Akertiya, Keratiya, Karakartiya, Karkiyana, Gunatek, Kunanakh, etc. Moreover, Fren indicates that each of these Arabic names can be read in about 24 varying ways and their spelling also varies in different authors' works. It is thus evident that an effort to identify these names is rather vain. More information is gained from an examination of the indicated points, the distance between them and their description given in the text. In any case, no reliable identification can be arrived at unless the Arabists and historical geographers undertake a thorough study of pertinent archeological material and compare them with works of other geographers. For the present, the names given by K. Miller and Jaubert should be accepted. From a cursory examination, Idrisi's maps do not appear influenced by the Ptolemaic maps found in the Byzantine manuscripts of the *Geographia*. Thus they must not have been available to him, or he chose to ignore them [Bagrow(1964)58]. The latter possibility seems unlikely.

TABLE II

Different readings in the MSS, according to Tallgren-Tuulio	Definitive reading according to Tallgren-Tuulio	K. Miller's transcription	Miller's (M) or Tallgren-Tuulio's (T) Identification
hbtr, htyr, hntyr	hulm (a) gara	Gintiar	T = Novgorod M = near Vilna
bwrdh, (b?) wgrdh	nugradata	sarada	M = Ardatov T = Novgorod
cwnw, crnw, mh(b?) wnh	curtau	sarnu	T = Serdobol M = Near Libava
srmly, srly	sunuboli	sormeli	T = Snovsk M = Priemyshev
snwbly, hnwbly	s (u) nubuli	sinuboli	T = Snovsk* M = Bobruysk or Mogilev

*Unclear in Bagrow's handwritten manuscript.

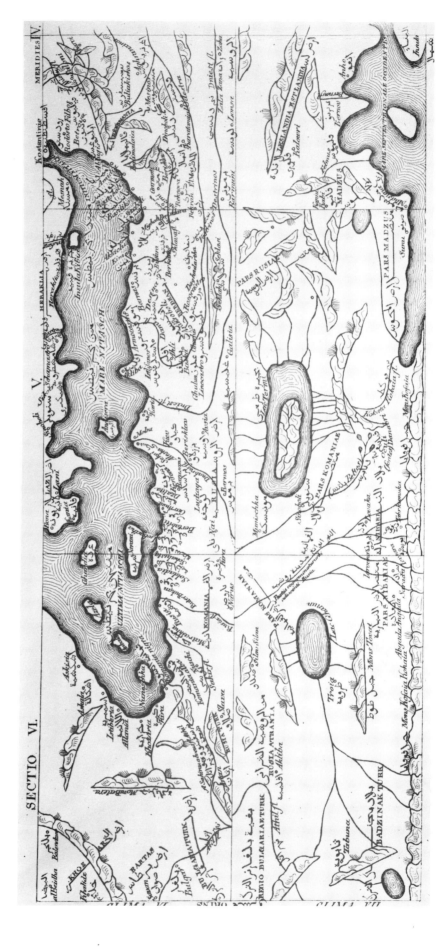

FIGURE 5. A hand-drawn copy of that part of Idrisi's large map which represents Russian lands. Note the orientation with south, and the Black Sea, at the top. Reduced (7:6) from Lelewel(1857) courtesy The British Library Board.

CHAPTER 1: OF SCYTHIA AND SARMATIA

1. The account of Sesostris' campaigns in Scythia and the question of the identity of the Colchians vis-à-vis the Egyptians is contained in Book II, Chapters 102-106 of the *History of Herodotus*. The editor has referred to the translation by George Rawlinson (2 vol., London and Toronto: J.M. Dent, 1910).

   Apollo of Rhodes also refers in his *Argonautica* [Book IV, 272-81] to some maps surviving from the Egyptian campaign in Scythia on which were recorded the routes and boundaries of the Colchis.

2. There is an extensive literature on Ptolemy's *Geographia*, of which we mention only a few selections. Bagrow gives both a brief resumé [(1964)34f] and an extensive and detailed analysis (1945) of the origin of Ptolemy's *Georgraphia*. Fischer(1932) reproduces photographically a Greek manuscript with maps, and states a position opposite to that of Bagrow concerning the authorship of the maps. Mżik(1915) and (1938) and Kubitschek(1934) and (1935a) have also contributed considerable analysis. For English language readers, Brown(1949) and Polaschek(1959) offer comment, Stevenson(1932) a translation of the *Geographia*, and Stahl(1953) a selected bibliography.

3. See Schnabel(1930) and (1938). Unfortunately, owing to Schnabel's illness, the latter work remained unfinished. It was completed and revised by its editor, K.F. Koehlers, whose point of view did not always agree with the author's. As a result, it is not always possible to distinguish Schnabel's original conclusions.

   See also Schütte(1916) and (1917), and Herrmann(1930).

4. There are, however, other sections in the *Geographia* which give significant attention to future Russian lands:
   1) Book V, Chapter 9 (the 3rd map of Asia) - Trans-Caucasia;
   2) Book V, Chapter 13 (the 7th map of Asia) - the Caspian and the land immediately to the east;
   3) Book V, Chapter 14 (the 8th map of Asia) - areas to the east of those in the 7th map.
   However, Bagrow has not included a detailed discussion of their materials related to the Russian lands, and has not fully explained their omission beyond stating that much of the information in these sections is quite fanciful. Certainly Bagrow was not indifferent to these areas, as his first scholarly work (1912a) was on the Caspian Sea; this interest will be examined more closely in the second volume of this work, in the context of Russian cartography.

   The editor has not attempted any analysis of these maps, believing that this should be undertaken by someone with the prerequisite understanding of the complexities of the cultural past in Central Asia. However, there is no doubt that our understanding of the *Geographia* will be incomplete until such an analysis appears.

5. Briefly, the positions of these towns, according to the maps of Version A, are as follows:
   Gamirakha (Tamyrica) is situated on the Sinus Carcinitvs (Karkinitskiy Zaliv).
   Navar (Naubarum) - at the sources of the Carcinitvs Flv.
   Olvia (Olbia) - on the lower course of the Borysthenes.
   Theodosia - on the south coast of the Tavrica Chersonesvs (the Crimea).
   Pantikapea - on the west coast of the Cimmerivn Bosphorvs (Kerchenskiy Proliv).
   Ermonassa (Hermonasa) - on the south coast of the Achillevm Promontorivm.
   Inanfia (Oenanthia) - on the south coast of the Taman' Peninsula.
   Tanaid (Tanais) - in the Delta of the Tanais Flvvivs.
   Tiramba (Tyramba) - on the southeast coast of the Palvdes Maeotides.
   Navarida (Naubaxis) - on the bank of the Tanais, on the middle of its southern course.

6. On the other hand, the general map on four sheets, usually appended to Version B, should be attributed to the late Byzantine period, and perhaps to the authorship of the well-known polyhistor Nikrephorus Gregoras (1299-1359). See Bagrow[(1964)36] and Miller(1931); the latter reproduces both general maps.

   We will not discuss the map of Version B as it contains scarcely anything new in respect to Sarmatia, although the Caspian has acquired a somewhat different shape. Reproductions of some of these variations are in Bagrow(1912a), (1918) and (1956).

7. In Roman times, the name "Agathos Daimon", or the "Good Genius", is associated with an indwelling spirit, such as might be found in a powerful person, a river, or an animal. As such, the name would be the subject of toasts and perhaps other ritualistic tributes, but would unlikely be used as the name of an individual. Later, as in Byzantine times, the name might be taken as a name of a good omen by an individual.

CHAPTER 2: MEDITERRANEAN CONCEPTS

8. *The Natural History of Caius Plinius Secundus*, translated by John Bostock and H.T. Riley. London: George Bell, 1893. 2 vols.

9. Pliny does note that all the seas take rise in the Black Sea as the tide is always running out of the Euxine and there is no ebb [IV,27] - an ancient observation of the surface outflow of fresh water that is replaced by subsurface saltier water from the Aegean Sea, and hence unobserved.

10. The map is now in the Nationalbibliothek, Wien, not in its previous roll-form (682x34), but in 11 separate sheets. The twelfth sheet, now missing, presumably indicates the name of the map's author. Bagrow[(1964)37-38] discusses these matters in greater detail. See also K. Miller(1916), which includes a complete bibliography, and his (1929); and Freytag Drabbe(1938) who attempts to check the deformation of the "projection". The map was reproduced by collotype in 1888 at Wien, and also in Yusuf Kamal(1926-1961)II, Part II, 235-237.

11. According to C. Muller[(1855)415], an anonymous periplus of the Euxine of about 400 A.D. indicates that Theodosia is called "Arbabda" or "Ardauda" in the language of the Alans and Taurs.

    Cumont describes and includes a color reproduction of the fragment in (1925a), (1925b) and (1926).

12. For a more comprehensive statement by Bagrow on these and other questions of Arabic cartography, see his [(1945)338f] and [(1964)53-58]. A number of reproductions of Arabic maps are given in Yusuf Kamal(1926-1951) and Miller(1926-1931).

13. According to Mžik[(1915)152], this and three other maps attached to the manuscript preserved in the University of Strassburg were made in the 11th century, and therefore presumably were not included by the author himself. Other pertinent literature includes Mžik(1916), (1926), and (1936); and Eckmann(1929).

14. The text of *Kitab surat al-ard* is, however, a different matter. Mžik(1916), who carried out a meticulous comparison of al-Khawārizmī's and Ptolemy's material, came to the conclusion that the *Geographia* had had a considerable influence on al-Khawārizmī's work. Mžik did not use the genuine Greek text of Ptolemy, however, but an Arabic version of it, "arabische Ptolemaios" as he calls it. Since the original text was published in Arabic and Mžik's work also gives the geographical names in Arabic characters, it is difficult to judge whether the transcription of the Greek names is correct. Mžik(1936) reconstructed a map of Eastern Europe, but a mere glance at this map reveals that it has very little in common with Ptolemy. The Black Sea, which would seem to be the easiest feature for al-Khawārizmī to represent, is over-extended in its east-west dimension, while the Sea of Azov is an enclosed basis. It is not impossible, however, that a manuscript copy of the catalogue *Vornehmsten Städten*, or any other material of that kind included later into the *Geographia*, may have been available to the Arab geographer; or, even that the eight books, at that time, might already have been jointed together under Ptolemy's name.

15. The one exception is the map of Azerbaydzhan which includes part of the southern Caucasus up to the parallel of Tbilisi and Derbent.

16. Bagrow reproduces two maps of this type: (1964)Pl.A in color and Pl.XXVII.

17. This map (22 dia.) was first published by al-Kaschgir(1915). From this work it was reprinted in color by Miller[(1926-1931)V,142(1:1)] and by Herrmann[(1935)23(7:5)]. Yusuf Kamal[(1933)III,Part 3,741(1:1)] reproduces photographically the original preserved in the Milli Kütuphane, Ankara. A brief note on one of its inscriptions and a reproduction (2:1) appear in Khasanov(1964). See also Miller [(1926-1931)V,70-74] and Bagrow[(1912a)18-19 and 76-79]. Another photographic reproduction is in Bagrow(1964)Pl.XXVIII(4:3).

18. For information on Russia provided by Arab travellers and writers see Fren(1823), a Russian translation of the Arabic; Khvolson(1869); Harkavi(1870) and (1874); Kunik(1878) and (1903); Westberg(1903); Krachkovsky(1937); Kobalevsky(1956); and Shumovsky(1957). More general treatments are given by: Lewicki(1956), (1949-1950), (1945-1954), (1956) and (1958); and Spekke(1938).

19. The Arabs also expanded into Spain via North Africa, bringing with them fresh ideas and new knowledge. Spain was then a refuge for Jews, and they represented a secondary source of information on southern Russia. The reason for this was that in Eastern Europe there lived a people related to them by religion — the Khazars. Trade and diplomatic intercourse were continuously maintained between these two peoples and provided abundant historical and geographical material on Russia. This in turn became available to Arabic scholars who used it for complementing their other information. See Brutzkus(1924) and Harkavi(1874).

20. Miller[(1926-1931)I,No.2(165x62)]   published six sheets of the 1154 map in color, and attached great significance to the map's use of color. It has also been reproduced by Bagrow[(1964)57], and Lelewel[(1857)IV,Pl. 35], a hand-drawn copy. Lelewel also reproduces, [Pl.37], in the same way the part of the large map representing Russia. This latter map was used by Vyazemski(1873) to illustrate his work.

    The complete text of the 1154 manuscript was published in a French translation by Jaubert(1836-1840). The areas of the northern sheets of the large map, embracing the Baltic provinces and Russia, is analysed in detail by Tallgren-Tuulio(1930) and (1936) and Rýbakov(1952). See also Minorsky(1937) for an abundant bibliography and some interesting data provided by the translator's commentary. Also of great value is Miller(1926-31). Here, among other things, he has reconstructed a large map after Idrisi, publishing it in color, and identifying the maps toponymy with that of today. These names, particularly those in the Russian lands, should not, however, be accepted uncritically.

PART II: MEDIEVAL IDEAS ABOUT RUSSIA

CHAPTER 3:

ILLUSION AND REALITY

With the fall of Rome, Christian Europe fell into a long period of virtual isolation, variously referred to as the Middle Ages, the Dark Ages, etc. By and large, the Christian Church, the sole intellectual centre during the early part of this period, inherited the cartographic legacy of Rome, and not that of the Greeks. There was no evident dogmatic opposition to Greek concepts of cartography, yet during the first centuries of Christianity, Ptolemy's map of the world was, for some reason, rejected in favor of the traditional Roman round map. Gradually the Roman concepts were modified to serve various purposes within the Church. Later, maps also came to have an independent existence or served as part of manuscripts. In either form, they became accessories to many medieval libraries, the inventories of which rarely failed to list at least one or two maps.

As to the areas of Russia, most maps of the Middle Ages contain very little of interest. Usually the size of the map was the decisive factor in determining the number of details included. The selection of items, however, depended on the cartographer, so that maps of related types frequently revealed minor but distinguishing differences one from another. For example, the large map of Beatus in the Bibliothèque Nationale (St. Sever Codex Lat. #8878) contains the following familiar names: Scythia, Sarmati, Colci, Paludes Maeotis, P. Euxinus, Riphei Mont., and Tanais. The map in Codex Cottoniana, British Museum, indicates three rivers: the Naper (Dnepr), the Tanais and between them the Ypanis. All three discharge into a sea, apparently the Black Sea. Meotides Paludes is not represented at all, though its name is found on the coast east of the Tanais.

Ebstorf and Hereford Maps

Special attention is due to two large medieval maps: the Ebstorf map (c. 1234) and the Hereford map (c. 1290). Although they are both T-in-O maps, their size, execution, and abundance of information set them apart. The Ebstorf map, a typical circular (350 dia.) medieval map, is oriented with east at the top and is centered on Jerusalem (Figure 6). Presumably it had been used as an altar piece, because Christ's head is at the top, His feet are at the bottom and His hands are at the west and east sides. Within the area of Russia, three rivers discharge into the "Evxinvs Pontvs": one nameless; the "Tanais"; and the "Meotis". All three cross a large lake — "Lake Meotides". The legend at the sources of the Tanais informs us that "Tanais was the King of the Scythians and the river separating Europe from Asia by flowing between these two parts of the World was named for him". At the estuary of the Tanais is situated the town "Gersanis" (Chersonese or Kherson?). The eastern part of the Evxinvs forms a crescent-shaped bay, "Lacus Cimericvs", which embraces the peninsula with "Temiscezii Campi" and "Oppidum". To the eastwards, the map provides only quite legendary information. The "Caspivm Mare" is shown as a gulf of the ocean. In the northwest, the Zapadnaya Dvina rises from "Rucia regio"; downstream are the towns "Plosceke" (Plotsk), "Smalentike" (Smolensk) and at the estuary "Riga Livonie civitas hic". East of this point, the river "Olchis qui et Wolkaus" (Volkhov) falls to the ocean; on its middle course stands "Novgardus" (Novgorod), and on its upper course "Kiwen" (Kiev). Evidently, the author had only vague information on the Varangian's route from the Baltic to the Black Sea via the Volkhov, Novgorod, the portage to the Dnepr and down to Kiev. The river by Kiev becomes lost in mountains in the south and does not approach the Black Sea.

The Hereford map, of a somewhat smaller size (132 dia.) is also oriented with east at the top and is

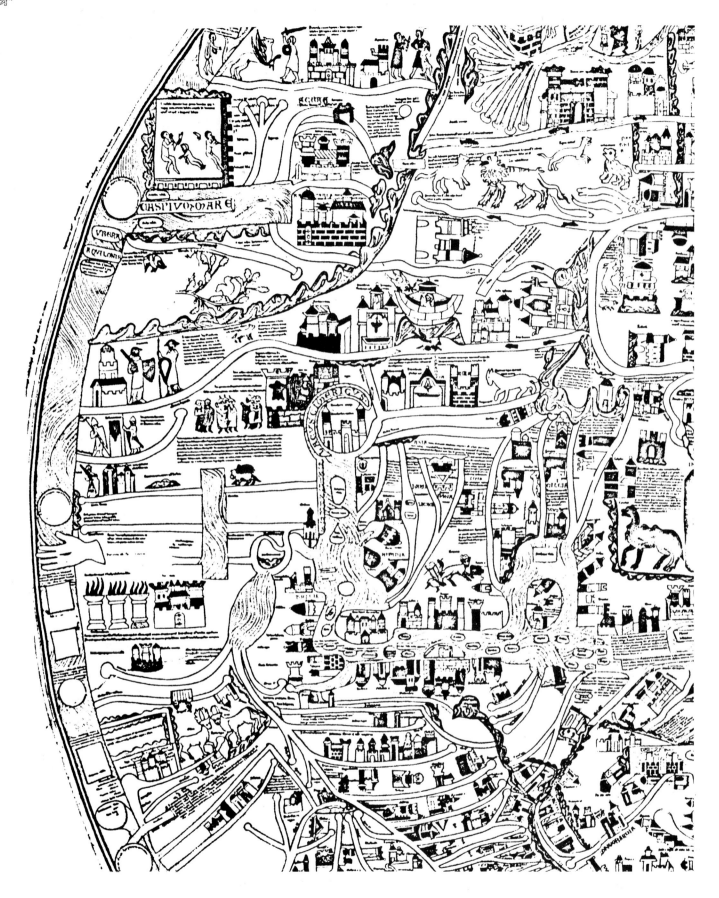

FIGURE 6.   Christ's right hand is seen at the left of this section of the Ebstorf world map. Jerusalem is just right of
the animal at centre right. Highly reduced (11:1).

centred at Jerusalem. [2] According to tradition, this map also had been used as an altar piece. It was found in the Hereford Cathedral, England, where it is preserved today. While it appeared later than the Ebstorf map, it is not as rich in detail and does not record the northern rivers. One small river, "fl. Danaper", discharges into the Black Sea, the central part of which is called "Cimerisum Mare" and the eastern part "Euxinus Mare". There is no other information on this river save that its sources are peopled by the "Alani sithe". Miller makes an attempt to identify "Oppidum", which is located on the river "Tize" — a tributary of the Danube — with Kiev. This town, however, is so far to the west that there is little reason to assume that it is meant to represent Kiev; our only clue is the information "Dacia hec est rusia". Between the Dnepr and the Meotides Rivers, there are two more rivers — the "Cornus" and the "Arfaxat". East of the Meotides are the rivers "Ylis qui et Jaxates" and another nameless river which falls into a crescent-shaped bay of the Black Sea, which is similar to Lacus Cimericus of the Ebstorf map. As for the rest of the details, they are of purely legendary character.

Having mentioned these few examples, their basic similarity to those maps of Idrisi is immediately apparent even though their sources of information are somewhat different. Neither of these types of maps, however, bears any resemblance to another group of maps which came into common use at about this same time — the sea charts or portolan charts.

Sea Charts

While the exact origin and development of sea charts is not clearly known, it is certain that some kind of navigation aids have always existed among mariners. We have already mentioned some of the very early *peripli*, or coastal descriptions, of areas of our interest: Scylax Caryandensis and Patroclus. Others include: Arrianus Nicomedensis (2nd C. A.D.) — the Black Sea; an anonymous *periplus*, erroneously attributed to Arrianus (5th C. A.D.) — the Black Sea; and Marcianus Heraclensis (5th C. A.D.) — the coasts of Europe up to the estuary of the Vistula.[3] Whether or not these *peripli* were accompanied by maps is a question that is still being debated. In all probability, sea-charts appeared later, having developed gradually from these written navigation instructions. Thus, the ancient *periplus* was gradually transformed into the medieval portolan chart.[4] We are unable to say exactly when sea-charts came into use as the earliest surviving examples are undated. The most ancient of them is considered to be the Pisan chart which might have been reproduced as early as in the second half of the 13th century, although the date c. 1300 is generally accepted. The first dated chart was that of 1311 by Petrus Vesconte of Genoa. There is no doubt, however, that there were predecessors although not in this perfected form. It is not our intention, however, to describe their development, but rather to comment upon their contributions to the developing image of the Russian lands depicted in them.

To begin, let us examine some of the means by which knowledge of the Russian lands could have reached the Mediterranean. The establishment and maintenance of the old Greek colonies on the north coast of the Black Sea necessitated establishing communication links with the mother country. As a result, descriptions of the sea routes were collected and constantly revised. When the colonies passed into the possession of the Christian Eastern Empire, continued cultural and spiritual contact was fostered by the church even though political intercourse was at times suspended. There were also interruptions created by the activities of various nomadic tribes from the steppes to the north and east.[5] By the 13th century another group began to frequent the coasts of the Black and Caspian Seas — the Italians.

It is difficult to establish exactly when the Italians began to appear there. South Italy was herself under Byzantium until the 11th century, and therefore access to the Black Sea would naturally be open to those Italians who were her subjects. The settlement founded near Sukhumi by Italians from Amalfi evidently was one of their first colonies. (It was called Malfitan on V. Maiolo's map of 1519). This colony was a trans-shipment centre for goods brought to Europe from the Orient. Beginning with the 11th century, Venezia's importance in the Mediterranean began to increase rapidly and, by a treaty of 1082, it was granted a number of trading advantages by Byzantium. In 1169, Emperor Manuel I Comnenus granted access to the Black Sea to the Genoese permitting them to trade with all the littoral towns with the exception of Rosso and Matrega (the ancient Panticapaeum [Kerch'] and Tmutarakan [the Greek Phanagoria, near Taman'] situated on either side of the Cimmerian Bosphorus). The entrance to the Sea of Azov was thus still closed to them. In 1199, the Venetians also obtained trading rights on the Black Sea. Some time in the 13th century the Sea of Azov (often called then the Russian Sea) became accessible to the Genoese. We know of this from campaigns they undertook, e.g., that of 1272, not only to the estuary of the Don but further upstream to the present-day Kalach-na-Donu. There, they dragged their vessels to the Volga from whence they could descend to the Caspian. This route, of course, was known long before by the Russians who utilized it as early as the 10th century. Also, Marco Polo records that "the Genoese merchants have only recently started navigating here; they have brought their vessels hence". [Bagrow(1956a)4]. The success of Lucas Tarigo's expedition to the Caspian by this route in 1374 encouraged other similar enterprises including an expedition which sought to find a shorter way into the Caspian by way of the Kuban'. Evidently, this was unsuccessful although a new factory, Chopa, was founded 28 miles up the Kuban' and soon gained such importance that a special consul was appointed to it. At a later date, 1428, Venetians are also known to have sailed into the Caspian for the purpose of piracy. We may presume that Italians penetrated even farther north — in 1350, a Lombardian was banished by the Hansa from a German bazaar at Novgorod. There were also Italians at Kiev as early as in the reign of Prince Vladimir. The Nikonov Chronicles [Ruskaya Letopis(1786)III,118] mentions "Tsaregradtsy i Nemtsy" in South Russia, i.e. Greeks of Constantinople and Germans. The epic poem, "Slovo o Polku Igore'e" mentions Germans and Venetians, Greeks and Moravians. In addition, various missionaries, writers, and explorers [6] travelled in South Russia, creating opportunities for obtaining and accumulating geographical materials which eventually found their reflection in maps.

The Catalan cartographers, the other important makers of Portolan charts, are also known to have travelled in South Russia and, after 1290, they practised trade on the Black Sea. And, of course, knowledge of South Russia was available in Spain at an even earlier date.

As to the contents of medieval sea-charts, there is little concerning the Russian lands except the coasts of the Black and Azov Seas. The normal Italian portolans are limited to the north and east coasts of the Black Sea and the entire Sea of Azov. Considerable attention has already been devoted to the study of these maps and particularly to the interpretation of the toponymy of the coasts of the Black Sea. [7]

Of more interest to us is the general description of Russia provided by some exceptional portolans: the map of Carignano; the so-called Medici Atlas; and the map of Pizzigano. Carignano did not content himself with the materials relating to the seas only, but utilised other available geographical data. The Medici Atlas also is rich in information. As for Pizzigano, he evidently was not a disciple of the Catalan school of cartographers and did not slavishly imitate them. Nevertheless, he borrowed a good deal from them. As a result, these three works should be set in a group apart.

Carignano's map, "Planisphère Gènois de Giovanni di Carignano", [8] has come down to us in a very coarse state of preservation so that it is difficult to read it correctly. The Caspian Sea, for example, can only be surmised from the location of the town "Organcha" (Urgenzh on the Amu Dar'ya) lying to the east of the place where the sea should be found. The whole of Europe is portrayed as an exceedingly narrow strip of land, particularly north of the Black and

Azov Seas. Here is situated "Kumania" and due north, the "Amazons". Due west, on the west coast of the Sea of Azov is "Gazaria". The Baltic littoral is occupied by "Cironia" (Kironia), Courland, Riga, and Novgorod.

Medici Atlas

The Medici Atlas, dated 1351, is a collection of eight maps: an astronomical chart, a world map, three sheets which form a normal portolan chart, and three sheets showing the Aegean, Black, Adriatic and Caspian Seas. [9]. However, only three of the eight sheets are of interest to us: the world map, the western European portion of the portolan, and the map of the Caspian. The Atlas map of the Black Sea does not differ from other known maps of this area.

The map of western Europe is very poor in names. In Russia, the Caspian Sea appears for the first time as a curved quadrilateral convex to the northeast with its longest axis running north-south. The river "Organza", formed by the union of two large rivers — presumably the Syr Dar'ya and Amu Dar'ya — discharges into its northeast shore. The Volga forms a large delta on the Caspian's north shore and flows in a straight line from the north where it is formed by the joining of two small rivers, one from the east, the other from the west. Two left bank tributaries join the Volga in its middle course, between the Kama and the delta. One more river (probably the Ural) discharges into the sea just east of the Volga delta. The Black and Azov Seas are shown in their normal appearance, although the Black Sea is connected to the Caspian by a river (called "Asso" in another map). South of the Caspian, on a neck of land, appear "Guriania", "Porta Ferra", and "Taffiliy" (Tbilisi). Into the Sea of Azov fall the "Sora" (Kuban') and the Don — the latter with its characteristic curvature towards the Volga. North of the Black Sea, a small lake gives rise to the Don and another river which drains westward into the Baltic (the Neva). Into the northwest coast of the Black Sea flow three rivers in straight lines from the north-west: the easternmost (the Dnepr) consists of two branches. Four other names appear prominently: Pr[ovintia] Moglia, south of the Neva; Comania, north of the Sea of Azov; Sarmatia, east of Comania; and Rutenia, on the north coast of the Black Sea, west of the Sea of Azov.

The Baltic is represented in the north, but of the names relating to Russia, only the following are indicated: Pr. Revalia; Chetelad (Courland?), on the coast; Leutiffania paganorum (Pagon Lithuania); Melbotsch (this is the reading given by Th. Fischer who assumes it to be Memel); and the island of Osillia (Saare, formerly Ezel [Russian] or Ösel [Swedish]).

The map of the Caspian is the first European map devoted entirely to that Sea. Hitherto, only one map was known to have been devoted exclusively to the Caspian (one in the Islamic Atlas). However, as represented here, the Caspian differs insignificantly in shape from that given in various Catalan maps; a few differences are observed in the place-names, particularly those situated on the west coast.

Finally, we should consider Pizzigano's map of 1367. Because of its content, however, it should be dealt with in connection with the following ten Catalan maps; the only ones (out of 29 known Catalan maps) to contain significant information on the territory of Russia:

1.	1320-30	anonymous, British Museum, London.
2.	1330	Angelo Dalorto, Collection of Prince Corsini, Firenze.
3.	1339	Angelino Dulcert, Bibliothèque Nationale, Paris.
4.	1375	anonymous, Bibliothèque Nationale, Paris.
5.	c.1413	anonymous, Napoli.
6.	1413	Mecia de Viladestes, Bibliothèque Nationale, Paris.
7.	1428	Jonas de Viladestes, Topkapu Sarayi Kütübhane, Istanbul.
8.	c.1432	anonymous, Firenze.
9.	1445-56	anonymous, Biblioteca Estense, Modena.
10.		anonymous, Topkapu Sarayi Kütübhane, Istanbul.
11.	1367	Pizzigano, Biblioteca Palatina, Parma.[10]

The general representation of north-eastern Europe is similar in all Catalan maps, including Pizzigano's. The island "Ezel" (Oxillia) is found in the eastern Baltic where discharges the river "Nu" (Nogorado in Pizzigano's map) — it rises from a lake (a large lake in Catalan maps and a small one in Pizzigano).

On the middle course of the Nu is situated the town Nogardo, Nogardia or Nogerado. Two other rivers are seen, one to the north and the other to the south of this lake, which flow almost parallel in an easterly direction. The northern one is the "Tir" (or Tirus — "the largest river in the world", as the legend says) which joins the river "Edil", which flows from the Siberian mountains in the east. Together, they continue southward in a straight line until discharging, in several branches, into the Caspian. The island "Zizera" is formed in the middle course of this river, below the confluence of the Tir and the Edil. Several towns are noted on the Tir: Torach(i), Rostaor, Tifer and, at the confluence of the Tir and the Edil, Bolgar

and Castrama. The river rising to the south of the lake is the Tanay. At its mouth is seen the town "Tana", and on its middle course, inside the bend, the town "Bercinan".

The Dnepr is represented in all of these maps as a very short river rising from a small lake lying at the foot of a mountain. From there it flows in a straight line to the south and discharges in two branches into the Black Sea. Pizzigano calls the upper course the "Branacha" and its delta "erexe". In the north, along the river, the town of "Branchicha" is indicated; in the south, to the west of the river, the name "china". In general, these names are repeated by the other Catalan maps.

A Franciscan's Map

At this point it is interesting to mention an anonymous medieval geographical description[11] of the peregrinations of a Franciscan monk, a native of Castile. This Franciscan (as we shall call him for short) was born, by his account, in 1304 and wrote this description between 1350 and 1360. From the brevity of the itinerary described, we can presume that he in fact never made this journey, but did so only in his imagination with a Catalan map to guide him. Of his "journeys" through Russia, he states that his route lay along the north coast of the Black Sea to the Caucasus, from whence he proceeded via Jorgania (Georgia) to Derkent (Derbent) on the coast of the Sara Sea. From there he went to Persia, Middle Asia and, finally, to the Gulf of the Dead (Mertvyy Kultuk) and across the Tanay (?!) to Sara. Then he continued up the Tirus to the place where it approaches the Tanay (here the Don); following the Tanay (evidently the Tir), he passed through the towns Baltachinca, Escleurza, Tifer, and Coranchi. All of these towns belong to the empire of Sara. Finally, he reached the confluence of the Tir and the Caspio, which rises from the Caspios mountains (certainly the Edil rising in the Sebur mountains).

At this point, the Franciscan inserts a description of the country he has traversed:

> "The Tir rises in the great Tanays lake, and both [sic] united form a very large river flowing northwards. The end of this river is not known. It flows into the barren and unpeopled country of Albizibi. Only a few places of this country are inhabited by vile people who have long, doglike faces and eat raw flesh and fish. Their name is Signofalos".

On his return journey, the Franciscan first went to the west (!) along the Tir (because of its great width he was unable to pass it) and arrived in the province

Sebur with its capital Casorama. This kingdom is situated between the Tyr [sic] and the Tanay. Then he proceeded to the towns Tascoar and Pidea, crossed the Tanay and arrived in Roxia [Russia to Markham] with its capital Xorman. This country borders on lake Tanay, which is stated to be three days travel in length and two days in breadth. It gives rise to three rivers: the Tanay, falling into the Black Sea (Mar Mayor) at the town Tana; the Tir, flowing to the Albirzibi [sic] Desert; and the Nu, directed to the Alemanā Sea, near the town Virona. The Nu forms the border between the large, cold country Siccia and the capital Nogarado. Then he returned to the country Xorman with its capital of the same name (he seems to have forgotten that previously this was the capital of Roxia) and then to Maxar with the towns Casama [Kazan' to Markham], Lasac and Monscaor. This country lies between Vogarado and Siluana. In reaching Siluana, he has already passed beyond the boundaries of Russia.

The Franciscan also passed through Yrcania, a country bordering those described above. He includes a drawing of its flag on which is found a special coat-of-arms which may be presumed to be one part of the family symbol of Yaroslav — a trident.

The numerous discrepancies found in these manuscripts, which not only disagree with known maps but even with the author's own indications, may be explained by presuming that he had at his disposal several contradictory maps and possibly also some kind of notes. Among those maps that might have been at his disposal include: the 1330 map of Dalorto, the Catalan map of 1375, and perhaps others. The former contains, however, relatively little information, while the latter is of a date later than that assumed for the compilation of the Franciscan's original manuscript. As to information appearing in his text which is not found in the maps, we must assume it was provided by some kind of missionary report, travellers' records, etc. Having no access to detailed information on all of the countries he described, the Franciscan, for the sake of uniformity, evidently limited his description to brief indications. We must also recognize the possibility that he had access to certain Portolan charts which are unknown to us today.

Summary Picture

The general picture of Russia as compiled from all the geographical material contained in medieval sea-charts, is as follows. In the centre of the country is a small elevation with a lake at its foot. From the lake, the Dnepr flows in a southerly direction. It is known to Catalan cartographers (in its lower course or delta)

as Elexe or Erexe, a homonym for the Greek colony which formerly existed there. The entire river is called L'ussom, (its Turkish name). In its upper course, some cartographers call it Branchicha, or Brinacha. This name appears related to Berezina. If the Berezina-Dnepr is assumed to be the main river-artery, the elevation should represent the hills at Minsk; otherwise, it would represent the hills of central Russia, "L'ussom-Russian mountains", as is stated in the 1375 map.

To the north of the hill is a lake which gives rise to the Nu (Neva) running westwards, the Tir (Volga) northeastwards, and the Tanay (Don) - southeastwards. As we shall see, even 16th century cartographers believed that there was a lake - Palus magnus which gave rise to the Volga, the Zapadnaya Dvina and the Dnepr. In Catalan maps, the Dnepr is excluded from this river system. Because of its absence, we can assume the Italian and Catalan cartographers had never themselves explored this region nor knew of the Dnepr as a link in the water system of the Russian lands. There is no doubt that the Nu is identical with the Neva because the water routes connecting Scandinavia with South Russia lay through Novgorod to the Volga while the routes via the Zapadnaya Dvina to the Dnepr came into use at a later date. In Catalan maps, the Dnepr is not connected with any of the other rivers. Thus, Catalan maps give a fairly complete picture of the river system. The connection of this system, however, with the Don is difficult to explain. In later maps, the Tir flows northeastwards and the Idil (the Itil or Volga), southeastward. The Franciscan's descriptions are contradictory; in one case, the Tir, which rises from Lake Tanay, and the Edil, from Siberia, join together and proceed to the Caspian; while in another, the Tir runs from a lake through a desert northwards and is lost there. In a map of the Ukraine, c. 1630, the Volga and the Don are connected via Lake Shat. The upper and middle portions of the Don are merely shown in general, without any detail, whereas the Volga is rendered fairly exactly in spite of its complexity.

In the upper Volga region, there were in antiquity several important communication routes. One was that leading from Kamsk Bulgaria via the Volga to Novgorod: up the Volga to the Mologa, the Chagodoshcha, and the Chagoda; a portage to the Volosh, and then along the river Syaz' to Lake Ladoga (Lake Nevo). Another route was up the Volga to the Tvertsa, up this river, a portage to the Msta, past the present-day Výshnyi Volochok to Great Novgorod. A third route lay up the Volga to the estuary of the Oka, up the Oka to the Zhizdra, up this river, a portage through the Bryansk forest to the Bolva and down this river and the Desna to the Dnepr. A fourth route connected Novgorod with Kiev: from Lake Ilmen' via the rivers Pola and Dem'yanka, a portage to Lake

Seliger, down the Selizharovo and the Volga to the estuary of the Vaguza, up this river, and by portage to the Dnepr. Finally, a fifth waterway, led from the Mologa, via the Sheksna and upper Volga to the estuary of the Kotorosl', up this river to Lake Nero, a portage to the Nerl', down this river and the Klyaz'ma to the Oka and Murom.

Catalan maps give a somewhat different representation of the route connecting the Baltic and the Volga: from the Neva, Lake Ladoga and the Volkhov, to Novgorod, and then via the Msta, Výshnyi Volochok and Tvertsa to the Volga as far as the estuary of the Nerl', up this river to Lake Pleshcheevo, a portage to the second Nerl', down it to the Klyaz'ma and via the Oka to the Volga. The towns recorded in Catalan maps which lie along this route include: Torzjok (Torachi), Tver (Tifer), Pereslavl'-Zalesskiy and Suzdal'. On the Tir is seen: the town "sclaujza" (the 1339 map), "sclay". . .(the 1367 map), and "Escleurza" (in the Franciscan's account). Buchon and Tastu(1839) read the name Perum in the 1375 map, while a Catalan map at Modena lists Peraz. These names are, of course, reminiscent of Pereslavl'-Zalesskiy, Klyaz'ma, and Suzdal' — all ancient towns founded several centuries prior to the epic of Catalan maps.

Also found on the Tir, or sometimes south of it, is Rostov (rostaor). This might be easily interpreted as Yaroslavl'. But as that part of the Volga on which it stands was used infrequently in those days, it probably was not known to cartographers. More familiar to them would be Castrama (Kostroma), which they usually located north of the confluence of the Tir and the Edil, and Carmancicho (the ancient Bulgarian city Kirmentchuk), placed on the eastern bank of the Volga at present-day Russkie Kermeni. Remains are found throughout this region of the ancient Bulgarian kingdom which extended up the Edil, now the Kama. On the 1375 Catalan map, a large number of towns are shown along this river, which extends into the Far East. This map further informs us that "the Edil rises in the mountains of Siberia [Sebur]", and the following towns, from the river's source, are seen: Sebur, Fachatim, Pascherti, ciutat de Marmorea, and Jornan. There are also several towns beyond the mountains: Sugur, Singui, etc.[12] Evidently, information about the lands beyond these mountains found reflection in the name of the town situated immediately west of the Urals. However, this town should not be identified with Sibir, which later became the capital of Kuchum. Sebur, rather, should be identified with Elabuga, near which is situated the so-called Chortobo Gorodische (Devil's town). This assumption follows if the town next to Sebur is indeed Fachatim, or Sachatim (the well-known Zhukotin near the present-day Savin Gorodok). North of the Kama is situated the ancient town of Mamadysh — a name reminiscent of the civitas Marmorea of the Catalan map. Jornan is

unidentifiable, but it may be Shuran. Whether the name Pascherti also refers to a town, or is that of the Bashkirs, is difficult to establish.

The number of populated centres south of the confluence of the Volga and the Kama varies from one Catalan map to another. They are especially abundant in Pizzigano,[13] but they are difficult to read because many of the names of ancient settlements on the Volga are no longer known to us. At the delta is situated a large town, the capital of the Saray Kingdom, near present-day Tsarevo. Where the Volga and Don approach each other is indicated a "pasagium", i.e., a portage. Within the bend of the Don is found the town "Bersiman" and a bazaar. This was the place occupied by Belaya Vezha-Sarkell. On the other side of the Volga, south of the portage, we find "Saline", i.e., a place where salt was extracted. This would be Baskunchak. Also named is the island Cigera — a name usually given by Catalan cartographers not only to islands, but also to land-strips between the two rivers. On Pizzigano's map the Samara river discharges inside this bend, opposite the island. On the same side of the Volga, due north, there is another river — "carabolam" (the Cheremshan, or the Sok with the Kondurcha). Saratov, the ancient city of the Burtasy should be located below the island. In Pizzigano's map we find here "taraga" and "sarcasi". "Locachi", on the western meander near the island, cannot be identified with Ubek, which is actually situated below Saratov. In some of the maps (1375), we also find "Agitarcam" (Astrakhan'), but in the majority of them it is lacking.

There are no towns indicated on the Kuban', while on the Don, only Tana (Azov) at its estuary, and the previously mentioned "Bersiman" at its bend. Occasionally, the town "baltachinta", or "Valdachinta", is located near the Don but in most of the maps it is located with a number of other towns south of the upper course of the Tanay and east of the Russian mountains. These include "Moscaor" (Moskva), "rasan plaslao" (Pereyaslavl' Ryazanskiy), and "baltachinta" or "Valdachinta" (Vladimir). Finally, two towns on the Dnepr, which we have previously omitted, "branchicha" and "jercasalar". The former is probably Bragin and the latter Pereslavl' or Berislav. Kiev is usually represented west of the Dnepr under the name of "China" or "Chiua".

Along the Baltic littoral, one usually finds Kateland (Courland) and litefania (Lithuania), both of which are characterised as pagan. They are separated by the river Sismaticis, i.e., the river's banks are peopled by schismatics. Of the towns, only Riga and Reval are known. Narva is known as Unguardia. This cannot be Novgorod because the latter is always shown on the Nu (the Neva) and is called Nogorado. Vironia (Výborg) is located north of the estuary of the Neva. Inside the sea, the island Oxillia (Saare). The country proper is named Russia or Ruthenia. In the south, beside the coasts of the Black and Azov Seas, we find Kumania, Allania and Gazariya — the latter occupying chiefly the Crimean Peninsula.

CHAPTER 4:

RUSSIA OF THE LATE MIDDLE AGES

Toward the middle of the fifteenth century, world maps begin to be transformed, as if they were competing with the newly found maps attached to Greek and Latin manuscripts of Ptolemy. While basically mirroring the traditional circular format, these maps include newer, contemporary information so that they may be said to mark the end of the period of medieval cartography.

Petrus Vesconte

We have previously referred to Petrus Vesconte; so far as we know, he is the first person who chose to practice cartography as a profession and whose maps are always dated and signed. His experience in drawing sea-charts could easily be applied to making world maps. His first map, representing the Mediterranean (and including the Black and Azov Seas), is dated 1311. It is likely, however, that he made a world map earlier: the first example of it, together with a few other unsigned and undated maps, is attached to Marino Sanuto(1611), a manuscript which is attributed to the period 1306-1321.[14] Of the ten maps included in his work only the first, the Black Sea (Figure 7) is of interest to us. His representation of the Black and Azov Seas conforms with that of a "normal Portolan" (as Nordenskiöld calls it). But the representation of features beyond the scope of Vesconte's competence reveal considerable deviations from reality. This suggests that there was a dearth of material at his disposal.[15]

As for the territory of Russia, he pictures it in his world map (Figure 8) as follows: in the northwest lie two adjoining bays separated by the peninsula "Norvegio". From the head of the northernmost bay, a great mountain ridge, "rifei motes", extends eastward almost parallel to the coast of the Ice Ocean and

stretches into Asia. To the northwest of the rifei motes, on the north coast of the Finnish Gulf, lies "liuonia". Into the head of the southern bay empties a small river. It flows parallel to and south of the rifei motes from a small lake to the east, and is probably the Visla (Vistula), and not the Neva. Just to the east of this lake is a small mountain from which two rivers run parallel southward into the Black Sea, west of the Crimea. The eastern one (the Dnepr) forms a deep delta. Between these rivers is situated "Rutenia". To the west of Rutenia lies "pomeraia", "Ungaria", "polonia", and "Gotia barbarica". Immediately to the east of the Dnepr two more parallel rivers flow southward into the Sea of Azov having risen in the rifei motes. Of these, the easternmost is the "Tanay". The number of these rivers varies, however, from one manuscript to another — thus there may be one, two, three or four rivers.[16]

Particularly characteristic of all of these manuscripts is the presence of two Caspian Seas. The first of these lies just east of a mountain range extending southward from and at right angles to the rifei motes. Its shape is essentially a right triangle standing on an E-W leg with its hypotenuse running NW-SE, and is named "Mari caspis yrcanu de sara". The second sea, lying further to the east, across another range of mountains ("motes caspii"), is called "mare caspiu." Its shape, essentially square, is similar to that given in Idrisi and it contains three islands.

Paolino and Mela

Two other maps of 1320 bear a great resemblance to those of Vesconte. They are a map of the world and a map of Palestine which are included in a chronicle compiled by the minorite Paolino.[17] These maps closely resemble those of Vesconte but certain differences in detail can be observed. As in Vesconte's maps, there are two Caspian Seas and their configuration is similar to that in the Vatican example of Vesconte. On the other hand, the western sea in the Paris example is more like that of later Catalan maps. In both of Paolino's maps we find the river Otil: in the Vatican example it forms a bend directed towards the Tanay; in the Paris example both rivers run parallel in wavy lines. Only the Tanay falls into the Sea of Azov. On the other hand, Sanuto omits the Volga altogether and its basin is separated from the Don by a chain of mountains. This difference between Sanuto's maps and those of Paolino can only be explained by assuming that not all the manuscripts were illustrated by the same person. Further, each had information from different sources which they added to Vesconte's map. Thus we can presume that the Vatican manuscript of Paolino was compiled at a date later than 1320. As to the Paris example, it was probably prepared still later since the shape of the Caspian had already been altered.[18]

A map[19] inserted by Pomponius Mela (Pirrus de Noha) in his *Cosmography* is also reminiscent of the style of Catalan draftsmanship. The outline of the Caspian is similar to that of the Catalan maps while the river system still conforms to that of Ptolemy. One feature of special interest is a mountain-ridge running north-south in central Russia. From its eastern side flows the Tanais and from its western side another river which discharges into the Baltic. Russia is located due south of this nameless river. The figure of the Baltic is obviously borrowed from late Catalan maps while the whole of Scandinavia is represented as a massive peninsula which is not (as in Clavus) joined to Greenland.

de Virga and Bianco

A more detailed, although more confusing, map is that of Albertino de Virga. The map[20] is dated although the last figure is not clear. In Wieser's opinion (1912) it should be dated 1411 or 1415. In respect to Russia, this map shows a river, in the countries "Samosira" and "Unia", which flows from the north (rising from the Ice Ocean) and discharges into the northeast corner of the Baltic. Into the lower portion of this river falls another one from far to the east. This latter river, in its northern course, is the Neva with Lake Ladoga or Il'men'; in its middle course, it is the Volga with the Kama; in the south it runs down a mountain-ridge in the Caucasus instead of discharging into the Caspian, which lies east of it. Another river, which joins the first mentioned northern river near its estuary, forms a large delta in the south with both distributaries discharging into the Sea of Azov. This is the Tana. Instead of the Dnepr there is a small

rivulet. However, the principal defects of this map, when compared with other contemporary maps, are that the main waterway of the Neva-Novgorod-Volga does not reach the Caspian and, secondly, the important Don and Neva-Volga rivers do not reach the Baltic Sea directly but enter first some other northern river.

Another Venetian cartographer, Andrea Bianco, also attached a world map (Figure 9) to his atlas of sea-charts (1436). Unfortunately, it is very superficial and poor in detail. In Russia, the Dnepr is represented as an insignificant river rising from a lake. The Tanai rises in a mountain block in the north. The Volga is "T" shaped and discharges into the Caspian. Although several towns are indicated on the Volga, all of them are nameless with the exception of "castorina", situated on its western bank. To the north of the mountain block, which gives rise to the Tanai, the name "rosie" is repeated twice. To the north of the Volga and the Kama, there is a tent in which the ruler of "imperio rosia magna" is seated on a throne. On the middle course of the Tanai we see "imperion tartareron". Despite the fact that his atlas contains individual maps of the northwestern coasts of the Baltic Sea and the Sea of Azov, Bianco, for some reason, has limited his information on Russia to these few indications.[21]

Walsperger and Leardo

World maps were also being produced at this time by others than professional cartographers. Thus, monastic cartography was nurtured by information received from pilgrims and missionaries from Europe as well as other parts of the Old World. An example of this type of map is that made at Constance in 1448 by Andreas Walsperger, a Benedictine monk from Salzburg. Despite its author's repeated reference to Ptolemy, this map[22] shows no Ptolemaic influence.

In the south, the Black and Azov Seas bear only a slight resemblance to that of Ptolemaic maps or portolan charts. The only place indicated in the Crimea is "caffadominorum Jannensium" — the principal colony of the Genoese. Of ports on the Black Sea, we see: "sauastopolis" (Phasis), on the Caucasian coast; "album castrorum" (Akkerman), at the estuary of the river "nester" (on whose middle course is located "Chyona", i.e., Kiev). At the source of this latter river, we find "yflandia", and just to the north of it, on the coast of the Baltic, "Rieg cat yflande". Into the "mare la taniorum" (Sea of Azov), falls a nameless river with the town, "Latania dominorum venetorum", at its estuary. On its middle course, the town "Saraa-caput tartarorum, ubi imperator moratur". Here too, in larger letters, "Tartaria imperium". This nameless river arises from a large lake

FIGURE 7.   The Black Sea of Petrus Vesconte as drawn by Kretschmer (1891a) from the Codex Vaticanus No. 2972. Slightly reduced here (4:3).

— "palus meotidis", into which a nameless rivulet flows from the northwest and its source, a tiny lake. The space between palus meotidis and the Baltic is occupied by the picture of a large walled town, "Norgadia cat rusie"; on the Baltic coast, "ambgis".

The Caspian Sea, "mare persicum siue hyrcanum ul' bacuianorum", is triangular shaped with an apex pointing south from an E-W base line. A river falling into this base line from the north has four radially disposed affluents, one of which is the "Cyrus". From the nearby countries named — "Kataya", "Sambortea" and "Corsamea" (Khorezm) — this river should be the Oxus (Amu Dar'ya) and not the Volga. Most of these affluents flow from a semi-circular mountain to the north, the "riphei motes". To the northeast, beyond the mountains, are indicated cannibals and beyond them, Gog and Magog. This brings one to the coast of "mare minus caspium" [the ancient Caspian as a gulf of the northern ocean still survives] and the notation "terra russorum iuderorum conclusorum inter motes caspios". Thus we can see that Walsperger's map is far inferior to the other cartographic works of his day; in comparison with other examples of monastic cartography, however, it is certainly an improvement.

More successful, though still inferior to other contemporary works, were the world maps made by the Venetian Giovanni Leardo (Figure 10) in the middle of the fifteenth century. Only three of them have come down to us, although a reference to a fourth is known:

1442 — in the Biblioteca Civica, Verona.

1447 — not extant, but reference found in the literature.

1448 — in the Biblioteca "Sebastiano Rumor" del Museo Civico, Vicenza.

1452-3 — American Geographical Society, New York[23]

All three of the maps are similar in outline but differ in respect to the amount of detail which they contain. Thus, the map of 1442 has only ten place-names relating to Russia, the 1448 map has about forty, and the map of 1452-3 more than sixty. This last map is typical of other Catalan maps in the names it contains and in its orographic and hydrographic features. For this reason, they are more like maps of 75-100 years before, i.e., those of Dalorto, Pizzigano and the anonymous Catalan map of 1375.

Another map, the so-called "Borgia map",[24] is thought to have originated at approximately the same time in which Leardo lived and worked. Since this map (Figure 11) was designed as a wall-decoration we cannot expect it to be the equal of other contemporary maps. Instead, the map is embellished with many drawings and scenes. For example, a battle scene south of the Finnish Gulf depicts either the ice-massacre or a fight between the Lithuanians and the Teutonic Knights. The configuration of the rivers in the Russian part of the map is characteristic of the Catalan maps. As to place-names, we see: "Costrama" at the confluence of the Volga and the Kama; "sebur ciuitas" along the upper Kama; "berchlina" on the Volga opposite the great bend of the Don, and "enogaria" — the reading given by the engraver but probably indicating ungaria; nearby, "boxiana" and at the estuary of the Don, "latana". The Volga, Don and Neva all rise from a common lake in Central Russia just east of the aforementioned battle scene. Just to the south of this lake we see a picture of fire worshippers and the legend: "hic pagani adorant ignera". Along the upper Volga, we see, "torachi" and "tifer"; to the southwest towards the Don, "Intania" — probably a misreading by the engraver for fl. Tanay. On the middle course of the Neva a nameless town — Novgorod; at its mouth, "riga", and to the west "litafani" and "careland". Thus everything is in the place we would expect for an authentic Catalan map of this date — the Borgia map being attributed to some time between 1410 and 1458.

An apparent representative of the Italian school of cartography is the so-called "Genoese" world map of 1457.[25] We stress "apparent" because it is difficult to establish a general model for Italian cartography owing to the small number of surviving examples of that school. In any case, the essential difference between the Catalan and Italian maps is that Italian masters (represented by Petrus Vesconte) showed the Russian rivers flowing from mountains in the north; the Catalans rendered the Volga in the shape of a "P" or "Y" — the western stroke of these letters began in a lake which gave rise to the Nu and, in the south, to the Tanay. In the "Genoese" map, all the rivers rise from the mountains in the north — the exception being the Dnestr which connects the Baltic and the Black Seas. All the rivers, however, are unnamed. The Dnepr forms a delta which takes up about two-thirds of its entire length — the eastern branch actually falls into the Sea of Azov near Perekop. Within this delta is situated "rossia parva". The next river to the east, the Don, also forms a delta in which is located the town "Tana". Between the Dnepr and the Don we see "Sarmatia prima". In the north, along the mountains, extends "ubi Lordo [Horde] errat". The Volga, formed by two sources, falls into the Caspian Sea. On the Volga, the town "Sara civitas"; east of it, "Sarmatia secunda". Between the great bend of the Volga and the delta of the Don, "Zithia" (Chechnya). Finally, in the Crimea, "Kaffa".

Fra Mauro

The last and most characteristic medieval world map,

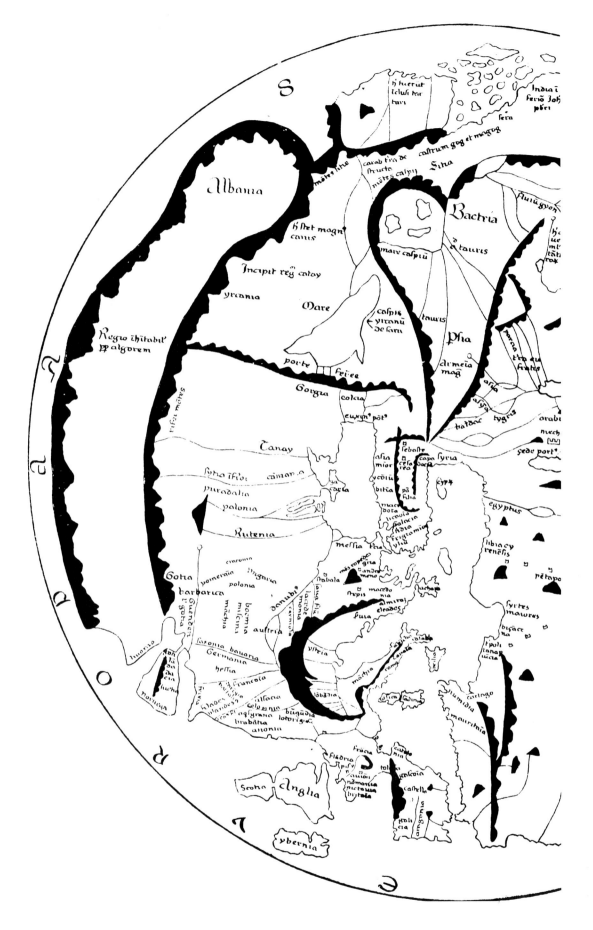

FIGURE 8.   The lands east and north of the Mediterranean from the world map of Vesconte as copied by
Kretschmer(1891a) from Codex Vaticanus No. 1362. Here at scale (1:1).

which may be regarded as the apothesosis of monastic cartography, reflecting simultaneously the traditions of the Church and contemporary geographical knowledge, is the map of Fra Mauro.[26] This map, apparently, was derived from sketches and drawings used during the period 1457-1459 in the preparation of a world map, which has not survived, for King Alfonso of Portugal. This later map, which was made in 1460 — the year Mauro died — was, for this reason, presumably completed by Andrea Bianco or another of Mauro's colleagues. It is marked by an abundance of detail which makes it difficult to distinguish the important from the insignificant. A glance at the hydrographic system of Russia confirms that a great deal of imagination was used in its preparation. However, even after eliminating all superfluous information, one is surprised at the wide scope of knowledge Fra Mauro possessed because his picture is unprecedented and would remain so for a considerable period of time.

Fra Mauro was apparently diligent in his efforts to collect any available information. For example, information on northern Russia was evidently provided by Catalan seafarers — the following note is written on the map near Permia: "una nave de catalani carga de corami *in mio tempo* scorse di qui e per desasio manzo el suo cargo". (A Catalan ship, loaded with leather goods, passed this way *in my lifetime* and to remain seaworthy jettisoned the cargo).

A characteristic trait of Fra Mauro's map is the absence of mountains in central Russia. All the major rivers rise from lakes and are inter-connected by portages; however, only once does the name "volocho" (portage) appear — in the steppe between "hiciche" and "chiovio". Despite the absence of large mountain chains, so common in other maps of this period, an inscription on the map notes that the Edil or "Vulga" [sic] rises in the Riphei montes. Also characteristic of Mauro's map are the roads connecting different towns and provinces of Russia. Information on the roads was presumably provided by travellers. No previous maps indicate them, although various literary works, e.g. the Arabian and Persian itineraries, contain descriptions of the roads.

The Volga, which falls into the Caspian, appears to be primarily a border between Europe and Asia. There are numerous towns along it: "Azertrechen Saray" (Astrakhan') and "Saray grando" in its lower course; "belciman" and "laivecho" (Ubek) where the Volga approaches the Don; in its middle course, the Volga divides around a large island on which are found the towns "chaterma" and "vedasuar". The "hoedil" or "carasu" joins the eastern water course and at the confluence stands the town "Castrama"; the western water course is connected with "fl. daraman"(the Don).

From the east, several small tributaries join the Volga: "fl. hacsu", "bianco"(the Belaya), "chocesu" with the town "Samar", and a fourth bearing several names — "carimanco" (presumably the ancient carimaspi or Arimaspi), "vorga", "chexa", and "carabalon" (noted previously in Pizzigano's map). In general, the area lying to the east of the Volga is quite confusing; doubtless it was based on hearsay, legend and some imagination. All of the Volga tributaries run through "ROSSIA BIANCO" and then also "Paluda rossia" (which is repeated several times) and join a large water course rising from the lake "Mar Bianco". The Caspian, however, is shown in a new and more realistic form — one not to be repeated until early in the 16th century [Bagrow(1956a)8-10]. The rivers "laincho" (the Yaik or now the Ural), "cur" (the Kura), and "tercho" (the Terek) also fall into the Caspian.[27]

Upstream, the Volga approaches a large lake named "Nero" which is connected by the rivulet "voxo" with another smaller lake. On the voxo stands "unovo grado" (the Volkhov with Novgorod). By means of another stream Lake Nero connects with a second small lake from which rises the river "hoca" (the Oka) with an affluent on which is located "Moscovia". The hoca, as shown, is either an affluent of the Don or part of the above-mentioned fl. daraman. This region, "Rossia Negra", is limited in the south by the "Thanay" — the sole river rising from a small lake. By and large, this part of Russia remained unknown to medieval cartographers. In Fra Mauro's map, the province "Lituana" lies south of the upper reaches of the Don and east of "fl. Oxuch" (Uzun or the Dnepr) which falls into the Black Sea. In the north, one of the sources of the Dnepr joins the Volkhov; another to the west, on which Riga is located, falls into the Baltic. West of the upper course of the Dnepr, the province "Maxar" (presumably Minsk, not Mogilev) is located; on its middle course lies the province "Raxan" with the town "chevo over chio" (Kiev). The river "turlo" (the Dnestr), with the town "jnocastro"(Akkerman) in its delta, flows into the Black Sea, west of the Dnepr. Between the estuaries of the Dnepr and the Dnestr, "Gothia. Fl. copa" (the Kuban') discharges into the Sea of Azov from the East.

Thus we see that many of the details are quite superfluous and only spoil the general picture presented by the map. The gravest incongruity is Mar Biancho. Zurla assumes that it represents Lake Baikal. This could not be so because there were no Russian settlements in this region in the middle of the fifteenth century — indeed Russian penetration only began with Yermak's first expedition in 1581. In addition, we see the names Rossia Biancha and paluda rossia on the map close by Mar Biancho. Thus the error consists in having placed the "White Lake" too far to the east. Normally, maps of the sixteenth and seventeenth centuries located it in northwestern Russia, somewhere near Finland. It would be impossible here to describe all the details and to analyse the information provided in Fra Mauro's map. It deserves, however, much more attention than can be given here or indeed has been given to it in the literature.

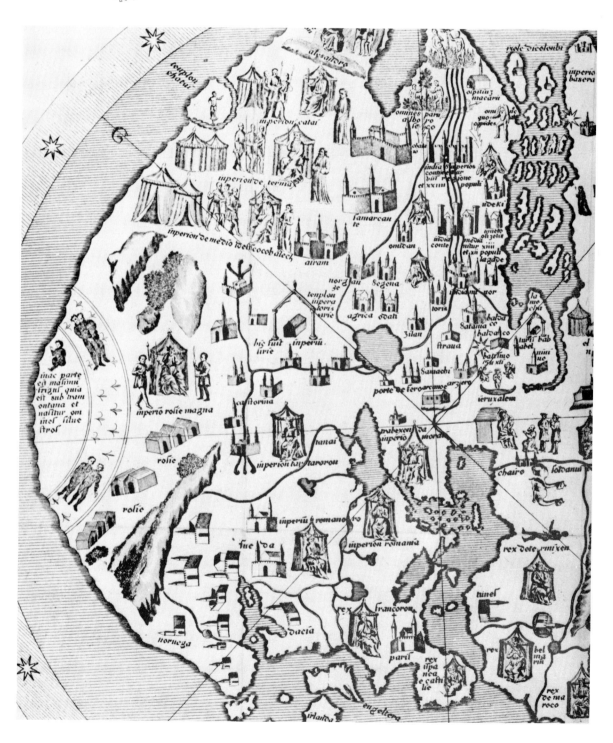

FIGURE 9. Portion of Bianco's world map of 1436 with its "T" shaped Volga. Reproduced at scale from Formaleoni (1788), (1:1).

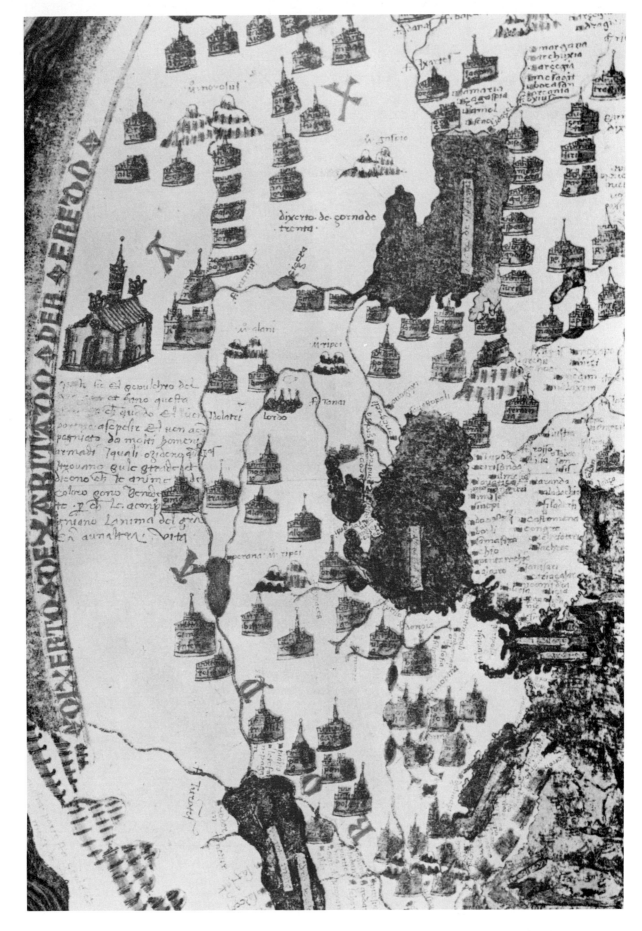

FIGURE 10. Part of Leardo's world map of 1452-53 showing lands east and north of the Mediterranean. Reproduced here at half scale (2:1) courtesy of the American Geographical Society.

FIGURE 11. Bottom half of the "Borgia map" as reproduced (8:3) from Almagià and Destombes(1964). Note the unusual orientation with east at the left.

CHAPTER 5:

EXTINCTION OF MEDIEVAL INFLUENCES

The fifteenth century was a remarkable century in its significance for the development of European culture. It saw the development of technical knowledge, the invention of the printing press, the occupation of Constantinople by the Turks, and the great voyages of discovery culminating in 1492 with the discovery of a new land hemisphere. The fall of Constantinople brought to Western Europe new ideas and interests in science, art, etc. through the impetus of emigrants from Byzantium. All of this stimulated the growth and bloom of the cartographic art. However, as with the transition from the Middle Ages to the Renaissance, it is difficult to state an exact event or date which terminates the Middle Ages and initiates this new era of cartography. Medieval features and practices slowly died out in the course of the fifteenth century and only occasionally reappeared: in the sixteenth century, a number of T-in-O maps, climatic maps, etc., were still included in reprints of the works of the fathers of the Church, Roman historians, and so forth.[28] In Russia, a T-in-O world map, the so-called "*lubok*", appeared in the seventeenth century and was circulated widely even into the eighteenth century. We will speak of this map later on (see Volume 2, Figure 8).

Ptolemy's Geographia

One of the legacies of Byzantium was the so-called *Geographia* of Claudius Ptolemy. With the decline of Byzantium (and the ultimate fall of Constantinople in 1453) there came westward a great migration of people who brought with them their various possessions of value. Among these were countless Byzantine manuscripts including Ptolemy's *Geographia*. Given the state of European cartography at that time, these manuscripts soon drew the attention of scholars in a wide circle of scientific and artistic interests. How-

ever, before examining them, we should briefly resume our account of the progress of Ptolemy's manuscript from 2nd century Alexandria.

As we have mentioned, there is a thousand year period during which Ptolemy's *Geographia* appears to have been unknown. Our story, at present, resumes with a Byzantine monk, Maximos Planudes (1260-1310), who was interested in and collected classical manuscripts, and who found and purchased a manuscript of the *Geographia*. By his own statement it contained no maps but he succeeded in making himself a set of maps exclusively after the text of the eight books of Ptolemy. Two surviving manuscripts appear to have belonged to Planudes[29] but this has not yet been definitely established, nor have we any certainty that Planudes' original manuscript served as the prototype for the maps included in the manuscripts of Version A of the *Geographia*. If this were to be proved, it would mean that these maps of the *Geographia* could have been produced at the end of the 13th or the beginning of the 14th century.

Without this confirmation, scholars have turned their attention to a closer study of the text itself in an effort to ascertain the origin, in time and place, of the geographic information in it. The author's own attempt(1945) has been by means of a thorough study of those materials which related to the Russian lands. We have previously referred to his conclusion from that work that the materials in the *Geographia* are not exclusively from the 2nd century A.D. Other general conclusions regarding the temporal origins of the rest of the text are briefly outlined here.

It would be vain to try and find in the geographical contents of the maps any information on European (Figure 12) and Asiatic (Figure 13) Sarmatia which is not given in the text of Books III and V. The mapmaker(s) not only failed to introduce any new materials but also made rather poor use of the materials available to him.[30] The difficulty in producing an exact map is due to the approximate location of many points (such as mountains, river courses, and territories of peoples) in such terms as "above", "beside" or "south of". Such vague descriptions gave the mapmaker great freedom of interpretation. As a result, the maps included in the original manuscripts are of inferior interest; the information given in the text proper is of considerably greater value and has received the greater amount of scholarly attention.

As to the material presented in the text, the main river system in Sarmatia conforms entirely to that presented by earlier authors. Strabo's error in locating the Hypanis east of the Borysthenes is repeated; apparently this information was supplied by a person who mistook the Dneprovsko-Bugskiy Liman (the Dnepr Liman) to be the mouth of the Borysthenes alone. As the first city on the Borysthenes, the text mentions Olbia (Borysthenida or Borysthenes as renamed by the Hellenes) to be northwest of the mouths of the Dnepr and the Bug. We know, however, from an anonymous *periplus* [ascribed to Skymnos of Chios, c. 90 B.C., by Cl. Müller(1965)229] that Olbia was situated at the confluence of the Hypanis and the Borysthenes, 240 stadia up the Borysthenes (i.e. 240 stadia from the mouth of the Dnepr Liman). Assuming 10 stadia equal one mile [Brown(1949)28], 24 miles is of the same magnitude as the present-day distance and tends to confirm the mistaken identity (i.e. that the Dnepr Liman was the mouth of the Borysthenes alone). Since the Dnepr Liman runs west to east, some doubt is also cast on the trustworthiness of Olbia's geographical co-ordinates which would place it northwest of the Dnepr mouth. After Olbia, the first town up the Borysthenes, according to the text of Ptolemy, is Metropolis[31] and, higher still upstream, Serimum. From its given longitude, the Borysthenes takes on a quite westerly declination, i.e. it descends more easterly than southeasterly. This is further enforced by the longitude given a part of the Borysthenes near the lake of Amadoka. Bagrow is inclined to believe its longitude should be 56°, not 53°30' as given, for such a correction will give the Borysthenes a quite normal form.

Far upstream we approach that part of the Borysthenes on which are located the town Amadoka, the Amadoka mountains and Lake Amadoka. Some of the Latin codices of Version A of the *Geographia* show that here the Borysthenes forces its way through the Amadoka mountains.[32] The whole of this locality is peopled by Amadoks. Such repetition of the name indicates its relative significance. Bagrow[(1945)378] proceeds to establish that this region on the Dnepr was peopled by emigrants from Macedonia. Lake Amadoka, from which flows the Borysthenes, should then be identified with the present-day marsh-lake Irdýn' (reminiscent of the Macedonian lake Ardjan) near the city of Cherkassý. The cataracts proper were not known to the compiler of the *Geographia*; they

were known in Byzantium as early as the 10th century as Constantine VII Porphyrogenitus (905-959) gave a fairly detailed description of them in his *De administrando imperio*. That some of the manuscript maps of Version A show the Dnepr forcing its way through the Amadoka mountains, seems to prove that the cataracts were known to the maker of maps and he associated them with the respective mountain-chain. Thus considering this material, the date of the *Geographia's* maps should be ascribed to the late 10th or early 11th century.[33]

Macedonian colonization was not limited to this locality alone. The Chevins settled down on the river Guiva near present-day Zhitomir, (the basin of the Guiva is the only place in this region where Greek and Roman coins were found [Antonovich(1900)]). They proceeded northeast generally to Lake Ladoga, where the colonizers founded the town Novgorod. It was to become the centre of the five pyatinas of Novgorod: the Vodskaya pyatina to the north, east of it the Obonezhskaya pyatina, then the Bezhetskaya, Derevskaya and Shelon'skaya pyatinas. Table III compares names in the Novgorod region with Macedonian names from the Lyagodina region. In the Shelon'skaya pyatina we find the pogost (grave yard) Pazhirichi-Pozharevitsy, corresponding to the town Puzerit-Pazarakia, situated west of Soluni. The *Geographia* enumerates a number of the tribes populating these places "up to the Riphei montes" — the Valday Heights (Valdayskaya Vozvýshennost') and the ancient Vokovsk forests, whence, as stated by the Chronicle, the Dnepr, the Dvina and the Volga have their sources.

The Novgorod Pyatina	The Lyagodina Region
Vodskaya	Bodena
Obonezhskaya	Negovan
Bezhetskaya	Bezik
Derevskaya	Dremiglave
Shelonskaya	Solun

TABLE III

We have used the term "Macadonians" rather loosely as there is some question as to the real identity of these peoples who settled so far in the north. We will avoid this issue here; however, whatever their exact identity, information on their life and movements in the 6th to 8th centuries is very scarce. Western Europe suffered no aggression in those days from the east so that European chroniclers had little to report about their Slavic neighbors. With the Slavonians, writing did not yet exist. It appeared later with the appearance of Christianity. In addition, ar-

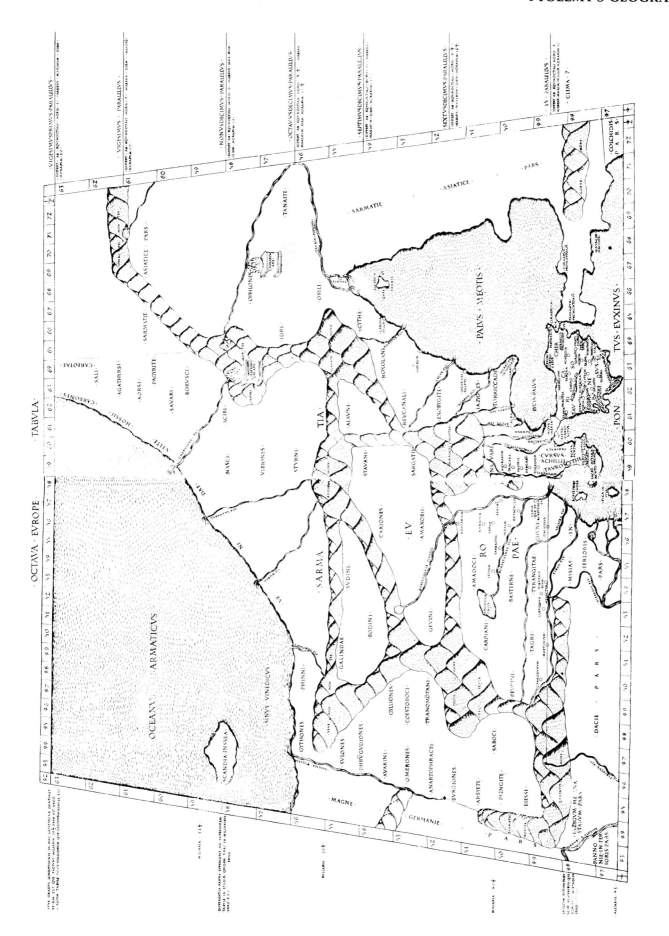

FIGURE 12. The eighth map of Europe, European Sarmatia, from the *Cosmographia* of Ptolemy, Roma, 1478. Scale (7:3).

cheological discoveries of monuments from the period of the 5th-9th centuries have not yet presented a clear picture of their movements. Probably their migrations northeastward from the Dnepr started in the 7th century at the earliest. No burial mounds (*kurgany*) prior to the 8th century have been found in the Smolensk district. The earliest burial monuments in the land formerly occupied by the Vyatichi belong to the 7th-8th century. Lake Il'men' was probably reached in the 9th century. From this problematic sequence of events, we assume that the information included in the text of the *Geographia* could not have been available in Byzantium prior to the 9th-10th century. We should not forget that the river route connecting the Baltic with the Black Sea, via the Volkhov and the Dnepr, first became known around the 10th century, as has been shown by the archeological findings in the districts of Smolensk and Novgorod. Prior to this date, even if any Russians occasionally reached Byzantium, they could not have provided any knowledge on the tribes of the north.

Knowledge of the north of Russia by the author of the *Geographia* probably did not extend beyond the parallel of the Neva and the sources of the Kama. To the east, numerous small rivulets and the Tanais fall into the Meotida. The latter river forms the boundary between European and Asiatic Sarmatia. On the estuary of the Tanais is the town Tana. In its upper reaches are some posts erected by Alexander and Caesar (these are referred to by Herodotus).

The Crimea, separated from the Taman' peninsula by the Cimmerian Bosphorus, is quite crowded with populated centres. Here is Hermonassa (one of the points we are certain was known to Ptolemy), Fanagoriya and others.[34] Beyond the Tanais and the Meotida Sea, there are no more populated centres, except for the coast of the Meotida and the northern slope of the Caucasus. A characteristic feature is the representation of the Rha (the Volga). It rises from two sources: from the Riphei montes in the northeast; and from the Hyperborei montes in the northwest. They join together and then flow toward the great bend of the Tanais where it swings away toward the Caspian. As we have seen, this representation was characteristic of many maps of the Middle Ages and is typical of the portolan chart.

As we mentioned, the *Geographia* reached Italy and its first Latin translation was completed in 1409. In this form, the *Geographia* gained much renown; initially it was issued without any maps and, later, with maps. Hardly twenty years had elapsed, however, before Western European scholars became dissatisfied with it. Thus, in 1427, Guillaume Fillastre, a French canon at Reims and later Cardinal of St. Marc's and papal legate in France, instructed a copyist to prepare an atlas to his order. The maps were copied from a Greek manuscript of the *Geographia* but the atlas also included a map of the north by Claudius Clavus and some remarks that Fillastre had himself written.[35] The map, in spite of its title — "Tabula Moderna Prussie, Svecie, Norbergie, Gotcie et Russie, extra Ptolemeum posita" — does not provide any relevant new material on Russia except for a few astronomical points on the Baltic littoral. This was, therefore, the first attempt to revise the *Geographia* with so-called tabulae modernae, and owing to them the *Geographia* gained increasing popularity. However, the example set by Fillistre was not immediately followed. To begin with, only a few corrections and additions were introduced, such as the modern equivalent of names which were written in parallel to the ancient names. Some of the maps were divided into two or three smaller maps, small drawings were added, or new maps were added either of a "Ptolemaic" type or circular maps of a medieval type [Winter(1953)].

Nicolaus Germanus

One "editor" (if indeed this term may be used) of Ptolemy's manuscript was Donnus Nicolaus Germanus of Firenze, who exerted much greater efforts in preparing his manuscripts of "Ptolemy". He redrew all of the maps in a new trapezoidal projection, altered the format of the maps and introduced new symbolization. He maintained, however, the same number of maps as in the *Geographia* i.e. 27. A few years later, Nicolaus Germanus introduced some new changes into his edition of the *Geographia* and included three new maps: Scandinavia with the northern countries (Figure 14), Spain, and Italy. In the map of Scandinavia, the number of places-names and details is even more abundant than in the map by Claudius Clavus. The Baltic Sea has no Gulf of Finland. The rivers of its eastern littoral are not provided with any names, but are numbered with ordinals, in Danish [Spekke(1948)46], from south to north: (after the Zamoysky Code) "furst" (the Dvina), "auenas" (the Hapla), "trodiena" (the Neva), "fierdis" (the Roderin).[36] The last-mentioned is in Sweden, in Roslagen. Somewhat south of the fursta is "Riga". Here is "Liuonia". "Primus liuonie Sinus" is written on the coast with the island "Oxilia" indicated nearby. To the north is found the town "Ungardia" (Ivangorod) which is Reualea civitas. North of it is the second river, auenas, with its wide estuary. Then finally the third river, trodiena, with the town "Nogardia" (Novgorod) well inland.

In the same year, 1468, Nicolaus Germanus prepared his third manuscript edition of the *Geographia*. In the representations here of northern Europe, he removes Greenland to the northeast of Scandinavia and Iceland is moved further north. The toponymy of

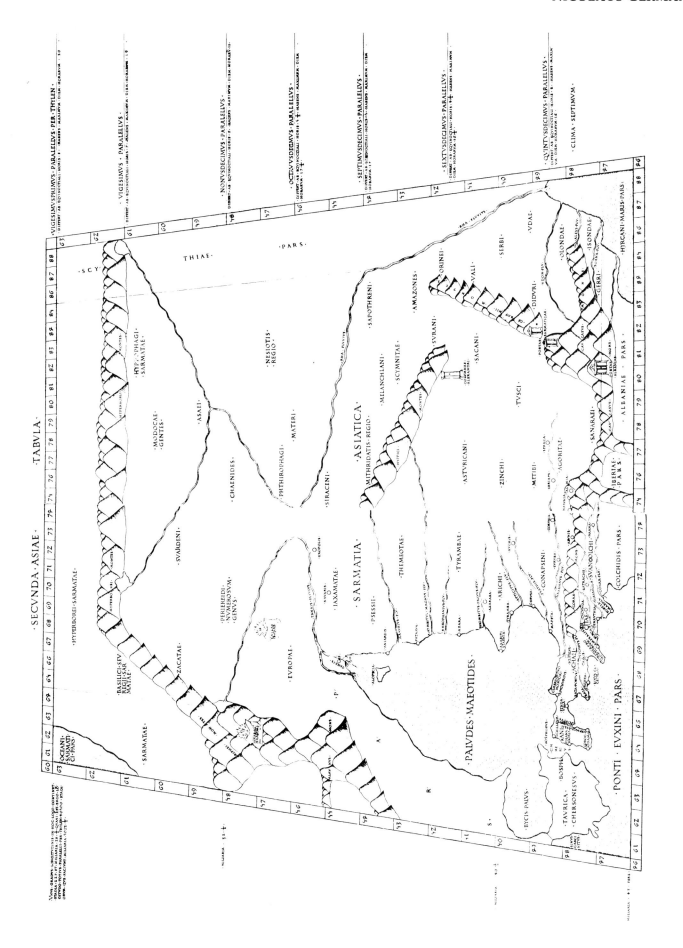

FIGURE 13. The second map of Asia, Asiatic Sarmatia, from Ptolemy's *Cosmographia*, Roma, 1478. Scale (2:1).

the Baltic littoral is reduced: there are no more names of rivers but only Liuonia, riga, nogardia, uirona, flantena, and, still further north, liuonia again. The Ulm editions of Ptolemy of 1482 and 1486 respectively were printed according to this manuscript edition. Thus the influence of the errors committed here are seen in many later printed maps and atlases.

Berlinghieri and Cusanus

Francesco Berlinghieri of Firenze also completed with modern maps four Codices of the *Geographia* which he edited: two in Italian were signed by his name and two in Latin were anonymous although J. Fischer(1932) attributes them to him.[37] The four modern maps which Berlinghieri included are Italy, Spain, Gallia, and Palestine. Moreover, he introduced several corrections and alterations in the old maps. Thus, in the eighth map of Europe (European Sarmatia) the Hyperborei montes are omitted; in the second map of Asia (Asiatic Sarmatia) Riphei montes join the Alauni montes.

The period around the turn of the sixteenth century was one which saw the diffusion of Ptolemy's *Geographia* in its numerous printed editions. Many of the editors of manuscript editions, for example, also produced printed editions. This was also a period when the cartographic inheritance of the Middle Ages was still further diminished. This came about through the process of complementing the *Geographia* with modernized maps, at least of those countries in which the draftsmen and the purchasers of the *Geographia* lived. This process was necessary because the original *Geographia*, while it was welcomed in Western Europe for its unique view of the world, did not entirely satisfy the demands of Europe for the simple reason that the place-names, with only a few exceptions, did not correspond with those of that day. Only historians were able to understand them. Thus the number of modern maps which were included in editions of the *Geographia* gradually increased: Berlinghieri's Firenze edition of 1482 contained four such maps; the Ulm edition of 1486 had five; and the Roma edition of 1507 contained six. By the middle of the sixteenth century, the ancient maps were attached to the *Geographia* only by tradition, and the number of modern maps began to surpass the number of old ones. Some new editions were published in two parts: Ancient and Modern maps. After Münster and Gastaldi, interest in Ptolemy's *Geographia* declined markedly although new editions — either printed from the old planches or new copies of the ancient maps, but without any modern maps — continued to appear every now and then.

Cusanus-Germanus-Peutinger

In order to trace the development of the representation of Central and Eastern Europe, let us retrace our steps to consider the work of the German humanist, Nicolaus Cusanus (1401-1464). A Cardinal, Nicolaus was a native of Cues [now Bernkastel-Kues], a small village on the Mosel. He is known to have produced a map of Central Europe which unfortunately has not survived. According to Fischer, it was produced in Firenze in 1439. Several surviving maps are assumed to be copies of this map. They are: 1) a manuscript map inserted by Henricus Martellus Germanus in his Codex of Ptolemy's *Geographia*, 1490 (Codex Florent. Magliab. lat. C1.XIII.16); and 2) impressions from a copper-plate, bearing the inscription: "Eystat. . . 1491", which were later acquired by Konrad Peutinger.

The new information on Russia provided by Martellus is minimal and confused. The map[38] is bounded in the north by the parallel of Memel; in the east it embraces a part of the Sea of Azov and the Black Sea but is very poor in detail. From mountains situated south of Prussia, two rivers descend into the Baltic; at the sources of these rivers, at the foot of the mountains, "Vilensis siuitas"; east of the right-hand river, "Mareburg". Two more mountain chains extend parallel to and east of these mountains: a large river (the Severnaya or North Dvina) with the town "Duneburg" (Dvinsk) makes its way between them. To the south, the towns "Tracha", "bilde" and "brest". The third mountain chain is broken off in two places and four rivers — two from the northern and two from the central section — run down to the Sea of Azov and to the Sivash respectively; the names of these rivers are illegible. Between the central and southern mountain chains, we see "Moscha"; here too is indicated "DVCATVS MOSCHOVIE". The centre of the Dukedom is occupied by a small height and somewhat north of it the town called "Zerchas". Two rivers, rising from this height, flow towards the Black Sea. The western of them has another, longer source which begins in some other mountains in which the town "Noua gradeca siue monagramman" and others are indicated. Finally, the river "Tirsas" rises from one more ridge, which extends north-south; on the western slope of it are located the towns "bristlauia", "synopolis", and "Sincoff".

The map found in Italy by Konrad Peutinger (Figure 15) also includes the westernmost part of Russia but it differs considerably from the map of Martellus. It is drawn on the same trapezoidal projection as that of Nicolaus Germanus which suggested to Wieser the close relationship between these two maps.[39] In the northeast, the eastcoast of "MARE SVETIE" (the Baltic) begins at the top of the map with the towns "Roderin" and "Flavtena"; east of them "Russiae albae pars". Flavtena is located on the estuary of the

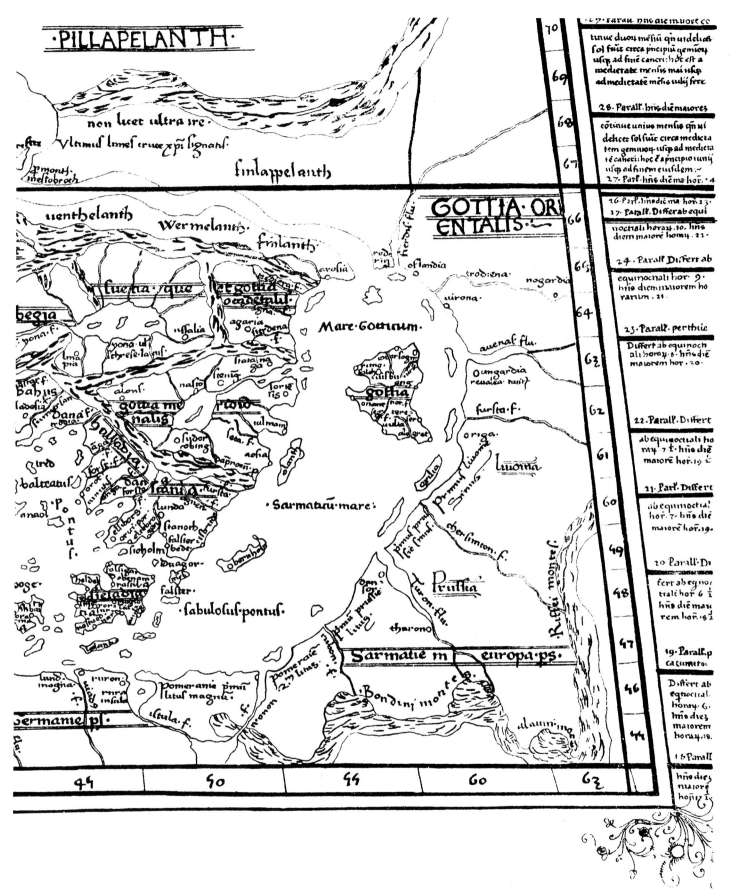

FIGURE 14. The right side of the map of Scandinavia from the Codex of Ptolemy (c.1467) in the library of Count Zamoisky, Warszawie. Slightly reduced (11:10).

"Narba" which crosses a small lake on which is situated "Revalien Ecclesia". A nameless river with the town "Novogardum" on it debouches into this lake from the southeast. The Narba rises from a large lake lying to the south, "Lacus Pelasa". Due south of the lake, "PLESGOV REGNVM" — The Dukedom of Pskov. To the west of the Narba — Lacus Pelasa lies "LIVONIA". Off shore lies the island "Oslia nis". Inland are found the towns "Silie in" and "Pornow". Two rivers, rising from lakes in Livonia, fall into the Baltic south of the aforenamed island. At their mouths "Partvs Porvov" and "Portus Saltia". The town "Terlatevm" is found between the first of these lakes and Lacus Pelasa (Lake Pskov). Below Portus Saltia on the coast lies "Riga". Immediately to the west, across a small mountain an unnamed river discharges into the Baltic — its two sources lie far to the south in the "Alanus" and "Amadotis" mountains. Along its right bank lie the towns "Marieborg" and "Dimenborg" (Dvinsk). The land on its left bank is "LITVANIA". This unnamed river is the Dvina (although the map names the next river to the west as the "Dvina"); its western source in the Amadotis mountains approaches closely to the source of the "Neper fl." (Dnepr) which falls from the eastern slopes of these mountains. The Dnepr with the towns "Chiavia" and "Comenia" along its right bank, discharges into "Bycis palus parts" (the Kuban') to the north and east lies "TARTARIE PARS" with "Palus Meotis" at the edge of the map. The Crimean Peninsula is complete except for its east coast; indicated are the towns: "Dospera" (Bosphorus), "Caffa", "Soldia", "Gzvngati", "Lemia", "Theodoics", "Cimbalv". In the south is indicated "DUCATUM GOTI"; in the west, "Padia" (Pilea?). The lower right-hand corner of the map contains the north-west corner of the Black Sea-"MARE PONT CVM SIVE PONTVS EVXINVS PARS". Two rivers, falling from the west, discharge into its far north-west corner. The southern one is a branch of the Danube, although it also rises in the "Carpatvs" mountains; near its mouth is "Album Castrum." At the mouth of the northern one, "Nester flv" (the Dnestr), lies "Nirum Castrum."[40]

Münzer and Beneventanus

Another map, which we can characterize as a primitive Martellus type, is that of Central Europe, 1493, by Hieronymus Münzer. According to J. Fischer, it is the most closely related map to the original of Nicolaus Cusanus.[41] Unfortunately this map is not very original and is quite poor in detail. In the eastern part, Münzer includes only the general names of the countries situated on the eastern littoral of "MARE GERMANICVM" — "RVSSIA", "LIVONIA", "LITTAV"

— and a few towns — "Nogradum", "Plesgo" and "Riga". To the south, "POLONIA", "MOSOVIA", and "TARTARIA".

Somewhat richer in material are the modern maps of the Cusanus type found in several later editions of Ptolemy. The first which provided some new material was prepared by Marcus Beneventanus — he probably obtained them from the Polish cartographer Bernard Wapowski and the scholar Copernicus. His map — "TABVLA, MODERNA, POLONIE, VNGARIE, BOEMIE, GERMANIE, RVSSIE, LITHVANIE" (Figure 16) — first appeared in the Roma edition of the *Geographia*, 1507. It is found almost unaltered in other editions of Ptolemy's *Geographia*, e.g., in that prepared by Waldseemüller at Strassburg, 1513. Its title here is: "TABVLA MODERNA SARMATIE EVR, SIVE HVNGARIE, POLONIE, RVSSIE, PRVSSIE ET WALACHIE".[42] Concerning the materials on Russia, "DVCATVS MOSCKOVIA" lies in the upper right-hand corner just east of "Silva Hircana" (1507) or "Silua herninia (1513) and north of the "Riffei Montes" which separate it from "RVSSIA ALBA SIVE MOSCKOVIA". The town "Moskia" is located at the foot of the northern slope of these mountains. To the south, from these mountains, flows the "Boristenes fl" which becomes the "neper fl." in the south in "TARTARIA PRECOPIENSIS". It divides into two distributaries which discharge into the "PONTI EVXINI PARS". "Kanyof" is situated at this bifurcation with "Kyow" just upstream. From north to south along the right bank of the western branch we see: "Cerkaszy", "Touanie", "Grottederon", "Batarezce", "flordeli" and "Laginestra"; between the branches is "portoborio"; and on the left bank of the eastern branch is "erezce" and "Mecaticho". Just to the east, on the coast, is "pidea". Off shore is the island "Zagori". To the southeast lies "Sinus Carcinitus" (Karkinitskiy Zaliv) and then "TAVRICA CHERSONESVE nunc minor Tartaria". To the west of "Silua herninia" lies "LIVONIA" and "LITHVANIA" and to the west of them "MARE SARMATICVM" (The Baltic). The River "Rubon" divides these two regions. In Livonia are shown the towns "Riga", "Marieburg Liuonie", "Smolenstz", "Treba ecclia", and "nouogrado".

Martin Waldseemüller

A new and distinctive representation of Eastern Europe appeared at the beginning of the 16th century; it was initiated by Martin Waldseemüller, or Hylacomilus, who published a number of maps in which he tried to bring together many of the new discoveries and geographical information that was being brought to Europe, e.g., the letters of Amerigo

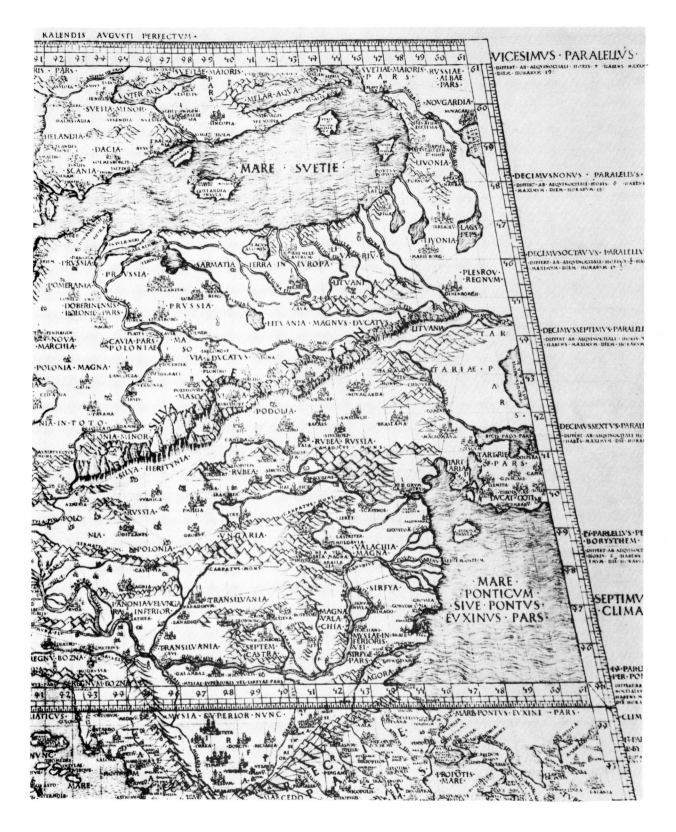

FIGURE 15. Poland, Lithuania and part of Russia from the "Eystat" map of 1491. Reproduced (7:4) courtesy The British Library Board.

Vespucci on the New World. He indicates, in the text of his world map of 1507, the source materials which he used: Ptolemy for Europe, northern Africa, and Asia; Nicolaus Germanus and Claudius Clavus for Northern Europe; Marco Polo for the legends in northern and eastern Asia; and the accounts of various travellers. For information on Russia the latter might have included the accounts of Ascelini (1245), Odoric de Pordenone (1317), Plano Carpini (1245), Marco Polo (1271) and Pierre d'Ailly (1417). This world map, "VNIVERSALIS COSMOGRAPHIA"... (1507), did not, however, achieve any distinctive new representation of Russia (Figure 17) for it is strongly reminiscent of Ptolemy.[43] The Baltic is clearly borrowed from Claudius Clavus by such names as "roderin", "reualia", "nugardia", "Riga metropolis", etc. The Baltic countries are separated from "SARMATIA" by a mountain ridge formed by the juncture of the "hyperborei montes" and the "Riphei montes". The former, in the shape of an "L", extend from a river in the north (which connects the Baltic with the Ice Sea) to the east into Siberia. The latter, in the form of an inverted "V" (the left leg carries the name), lie just to the south with the apexes of these "two letters" just touching. The Hyperborei montes form the watershed between the Caspian and the Ice Sea: "nogardia" is the only city indicated to their north. In the "Rha" basin to the south he introduces several names not found in Ptolemy: "loriman", "borga sapotrem", "lalachij", and "magna atroca".

Waldseemüller was more successful in incorporating new material in his "Carta Marina" of 1516.[44] A study of this map (Figure 18) reveals, however, that he had also used some other materials besides those previously mentioned. The representation of the Tzar of Muscovy in this map led J. Fisher[(1915) and (1916a)] to assume that Waldseemüller had utilized some materials supplied to him by Poppel. But Platonov(1922) destroys the legend of the German knight Poppel, who, travelling in countries unknown to Europe, was said to have chanced upon Moskva in 1486 and, on his return, to have presented Muscovy as a political and geographical discovery of his own. Moskva, of course, was already known to Europe at that date: a number of major architectural features, e.g., Uspensky Cathedral, had been designed and built by Italians; embassies had been repeatedly sent to Italy in order to recruit these and other craftsmen; and many other Europeans had gone to Moskva on their own initiative in quest of work — most of this traffic went by way of Germany. Thus there were many possibilities in Germany for information to be obtained on Muscovy before the return of Poppel.

An examination of the 1516 map shows that the geographical points are so arranged that different routes can be seen radiating out from Moskva — five

routes are discussed in detail by Bagrow(1962). The Russia plain is bounded in the west by small mountain ridges which nearly parallel the Baltic Sea. To the east, another mountain range (labelled "Hyperborei & Ryphei montes" in the Wolfegg Atlas) descends from a promontory in "OCEANVS SEPTEN" to the west in a uniform arc. It forms the watershed between the Baltic and the Black-Caspian Seas to the south. From two sources in its northwestern flank, the "Volga fl" flows to the northwest across a lake, with the town of "Novoguardia", and on to the Baltic. As we have noted, in the late Middle Ages the name Volkhov was frequently confused with that of the Volga; we see this here. Thus the unnamed lake is Il'men'. However, the presence of the town "Notueri" (Natverye or Tver') along the upper course and the name "mosca fl." upstream show that this river is also meant to be in the Volga system! To the north a second river flows northwest from the mountains past "Voluckta" (Vologda) to "LACVS ALBVS" with its cities "Beloser" and "Ustusch" (Ustyug). From Lacvs Albvs the river flows north into the northern ocean. Here we see the towns "Bemfeldz" and "Kargopolis". From the southeast flank of these mountains rise both the "Rha fl." and the "Tanais fl. sive Volga". "BVLGARIA MAGNA" is indicated at both their sources. The Volga flows to the southeast through "TARTARIA", past "Salacinit" (Saray); midway it is joined by the Kama (unnamed) flowing from mountains (also the "Hyperborei montes") to the northeast. The Don flows southeast then turns southwest past the "NAGAI" to the land of the "CASANA" and the "CREMANI" and "MARE MAIOR" (the Black Sea). To the west, the "neper fl" falls from the Hyperborei montes into the Black Sea. At its sources are "RVSSIA" and "nouoguardia", and near its mouth, "Ciuonia" (Kiev). As a whole, the Black Sea, the Crimea, the Sea of Azov and the Caspian are a repetition of Genoese and Catalan maps.

A characteristic feature of this map is the configuration of the northern end of the Baltic Sea. North of "flantena", on a narrow cape protruding northward, is "Roderin". Then, two deep bays — one extends to the east and the other to the west — which are connected to the Baltic by a narrow channel past Flantena. This is not unlike the representation of the Clavus type such as that of Nicolaus Germanus where the western bay is actually a channel separating the Scandinavian island from the mainland, "finlappelanth", to the north; the eastern bay would correspond to the fourth river. Of interest in Waldseemüller's map is the appearance of "Viburgis" [Výborg] on the coast opposite Flantena. This would allow the interpretation that the two bays were Lake Ladoga and Lake Onega and the channel was the Neva — according to Russian sources, the Neva was thought merely to be a sound of Lake Nevo, i.e., of Lake Ladoga. Consequently,

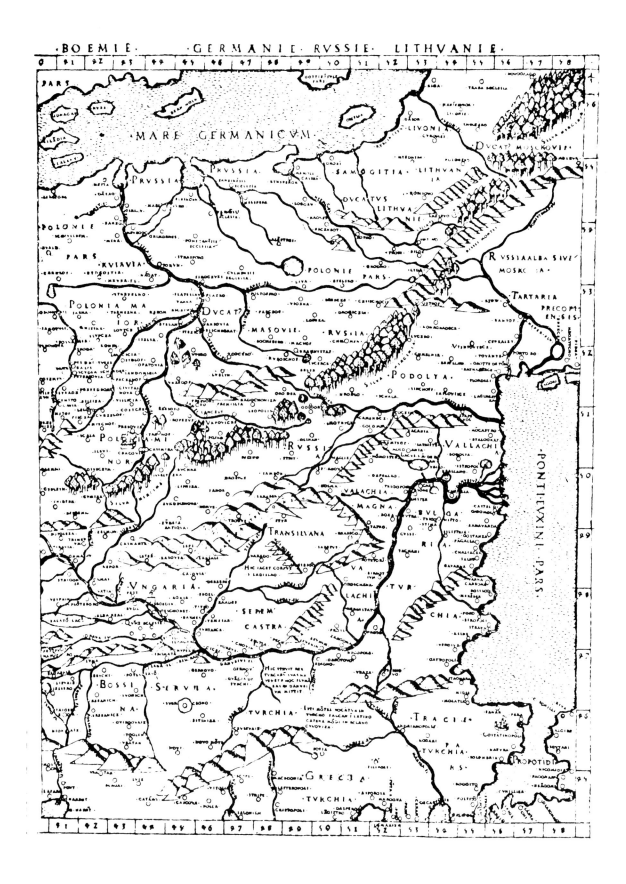

FIGURE 16. Right half of Marcus Beneventanus' map of Poland and part of Russia from the 1507 Roma edition of the *Geographia*. Scale here (7:4).

Roderin would be found somewhere on the bank of the Neva or on Lake Ladoga. In a somewhat later map (that of A. Wied), the town "Rogodiff" is situated on the coast of the Gulf of Finland opposite Výborg. This name had been given to Narva by the people of Novgorod in occupying it in 1294. The river Flantena south of Rogodiff is the Plyussa. Thus we can state that Waldseemüller in fact provides us with new and interesting material only in respect to Muscovy proper and circumstantially describes various travel routes within it. As for southern and particularly eastern Russia, the image remained the same as in maps of an earlier date. We should also point out that Waldseemüller was not always successful in collating the new material with the old: for example, the Volga appears in his map in four different aspects — the Volga-Volkhov, the Volga flowing from Lake Il'men', the Volga-Rha fl. and the Volga-Tanais. In any case, he was the first to provide Western Europe with these new materials — materials which preceded even those given by Matthew of Miechów and, in respect to Central Russia, those included by S. Münster in his *Commentaries on Solinus*, 1538, which were supplied to him by Matthew of Miechów.

Matthew of Miechów

The Canon of Kraków, Matthew of Miechów (Maciez z Miechowa) (1457-1523), was a versatile man who left to posterity a number of scientific works, three world maps, a sea-chart and a book specifically devoted to Russia.[45] Prior to Matthew, it was generally believed that the interior of Russia was occupied by high mountains giving rise to the largest rivers of Sarmatia. In spite of the step forward taken by Catalan cartographers in representing the Volga and the Don with a common source in a large lake (from whence the Volkhov-Neva flows in a westerly direction to the Baltic Sea), Ptolemy's traditional representation of Sarmatia continued and, on the whole, was dominant until Waldseemüller's day. Matthew was the first to venture that:

"The Ryphei and Hyperborei montes exist merely on paper and in the imagination of cosmographers. Actually, the whole of Muscovy is plains with the exception of a few insignificant hills, which do not even deserve this name".

Matthew describes the Volga's course as extending beyond the frontiers of Muscovy of that time. The Yugorsky Kray, whose people speak a language related to Hungarian, was already known to him. He comments ironically on the temperate climate of the extreme north, the land of the happy Hyperboreans:

"Such a contrast with reality — can one be called happy if one is bereft of everything, even of the most necessary? And how can one speak of a temperate climate in a place where eternal night reigns during the winter solstice and eternal day with a low temperature during the summer solstice?"

We know of one reaction to this declaration from the report of Francesco da Colla who, with Antonio de Conti, was dispatched to Russia in 1518 by the Emperor Maximilian. Da Colla wrote that a well-known physician and scientist of Kraków presented the Emperor with a work in which he dared to doubt the assertion of Ptolemy, the King of all cosmographers, that the Don had its sources in the Ryphei montes. On the contrary, this scientist asserted that no such mountains exist in Russia. The Emperor, who was familiar with cosmographical knowledge and was a great admirer of Ptolemy, was displeased and gave orders to invesitage this question. Da Colla's report, the result of the investigation, is contradictory and somewhat absurd in the information it gives on Russia. In regard to mountains, he states:

"All of the north of Russia is covered with Ryphei montes, among which there is one surpassing in height all others — this the Yugor from which flows the Don".

He again returns to this question:

"According to Krakovets, the country giving rise to the Don is virtually flat; as for the amount of water accumulating there, it is the result of frequent rain and is quite clear that neither the Don, nor any other large river, could have its sources — as Krakovets insists — in such country. The rivers rise much further north, in the Ryphei montes".

Herberstein, as we shall see presently, was later to confirm Matthew's opinion that the large rivers of Russia spring from different lakes situated in the interior plain.

Sebastian Münster

The little map which was published by Sebastian Münster in 1538 may also have included material supplied by Matthew of Miechów. When Münster needed materials in compiling his *Cosmographia*, he asked various scientists to provide him information on the various countries they had seen. These scientists included a refugee from Russia, Ivan Lyatsky, and the Ambassador Herberstein, who had visited Russia twice. Materials on Poland were provided by Johann Tarnowsky, Andreas of Gorka and Stanislaus Laski.[46] We can presume, however, that before mak-

FIGURE 17. Russia from Waldseemüller's world map of 1507, slightly reduced (10:9).

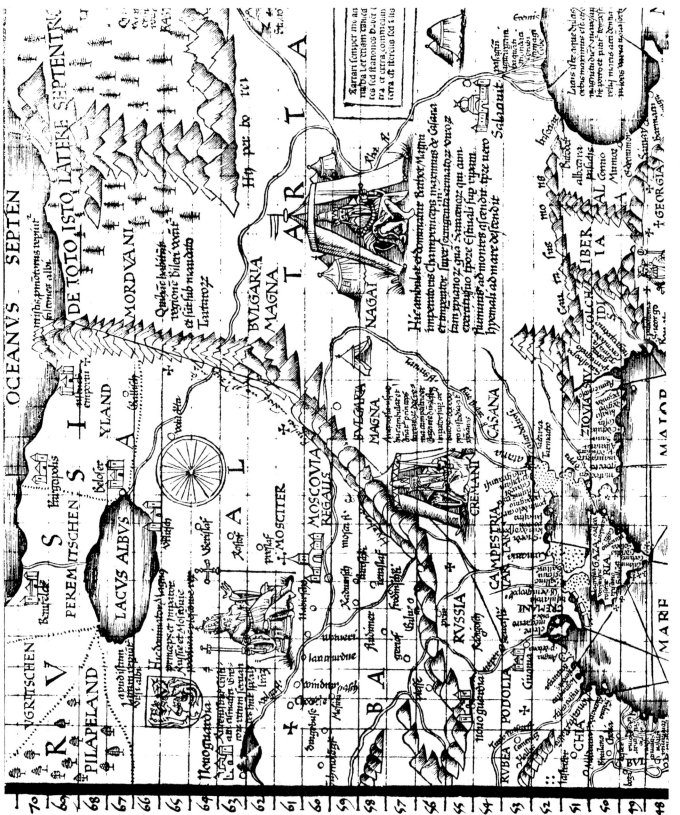

FIGURE 18.   European Russia from the Arctic Ocean to the Black and Caspian Seas from Waldseemüller's world map of 1516, slightly

ing a public appeal [simultaneously with publishing his (1528), Münster had written to specific persons with this request. Matthew, having died in 1523, could not have been one of them. Münster did have a sketch (Figure 19) by Matthew representing the plain of Central Russia where the main rivers rose.[47] According to Buczek, Matthew had not compiled this sketch from materials he himself had collected, but from hearsay. Buczek asserts that Matthew had never been either in Russia or in Lithuania and had compiled this treatise from reports of Polish military men, ambassadors and merchants. This would explain the error he committed in making the Volga debauch into the Black Sea. However, Buczek gives no evidence for this statement. The editor of one of the posthumous editions of Münster's *Cosmographia*[(1598)1256] adds:

> "diese Landschaften Moscovien, Reussen, Littaw, und andere mitnächtige Länder hat beschrieben Doctor Mathias von Michow, ein Poländer der Wohnung halb, vnnd hat sie vast erfahren."

"Ex professo" might mean that Matthew's profession placed these materials at his disposal. Münster might have been sent this map-sketch some time after 1517 — the year in which Matthew published his treatise on Sarmatia. The published treatise has an error regarding the mouth of the Volga, but since the sketch does not show this we can not make any other assertions. Even if Matthew had been in Central Russia, it is not certain that he would have obtained correct information on the course of the Volga and its mouth. In any case, since Münster referred to Matthew, we have no reason to doubt that this material was indeed provided by Matthew.

This small map-sketch is of considerable interest in that it gives special emphasis to the sources of the main rivers of Central Russia as known at that time. In the north is "Ladoga lacus" into which a river empties from the south. The river's east branch rises near the town "valtschach" (Volkhov) while the western branch rises from "ylmen lacus" (Lake Il'men'). Between is situated "Nouogardia magna" (Novgorod). To the east flows the "Rha seu volga fl" past the town "Tfezo" (Tver'); also flowing from the center of the map, but to the northwest, is the "Dvina fl" past "polotzko" (Polotsk), to "Riga". Finally the "Boryschenes qui & neper" flows west from the center of the map passing the town "Smolensky" and then turns south past "Kyonia" (Kiev) down stream. In the southeast, the upper course of the "Tanais" is shown with the town "Reschau" (Ryazan'). In the center the town "Mosconia" (Moskva). As we can see this small map presents a fairly clear idea of the plain of Central Russia. There are no mountains. But unfortunately, this was little known at that time or perhaps insufficiently appreciated by those who did. Evidently even

FIGURE 19. Münster's sketch map (at scale) by Matthew of Miechów as it appeared in Solinus, *Rerum toto orbe...*, Basileae, 1538.

Münster himself did not later rely upon it and used other materials instead of his *Cosmographia*. Thus we can state that it had no bearing on the works of contemporary cartographers. As for maps of a later date, e.g., Münster's 1512 map of Europe, they contain so many new details that it is difficult to establish to what extent Matthew's materials had been used in compiling them or whether they had been used at all.

CHAPTER 3: ILLUSION AND REALITY

1. The map, destroyed in World War II, has been reproduced in color by Miller (1896) V, (7:2) from an earlier photocopy given in Sommerbradt (1891) as an atlas on 1 sheet (8:1) and on 24 sheets (1:1). It is also reproduced by Yusuf Kamal(1936) IV, Part I, 1116(7:1); in color by Bagrow (1964) Pl.E, (12:1); and by Springbok-Editions, Inc., New York, N.Y., as a jig-saw puzzle (7:1)! A reduced (7:1) photocopy of the reproduction in Miller is appended to Yegorov(1913) who translates into Russian most of the legends on the maps (pp. 270-289).

2. The Hereford map is reproduced in two colors by Miller (1896) IV, (7:3) as a photograph from Jomard (1842-1862) T.XIV (1:1). Other reproductions include Stanford (1869); Nordenskiöld (1897) 15 (6:1) from Jomard; Yusuf Kamal (1936) IV, Part 1,1077 (8:3); Bagrow (1918) 11 (9:1) and (1964) Pl.XXIV (8:1); Crone (1948a) (12:1); and Almagià and Destombes (1964) Pl.XXIV (6:1). Crone (1948b) reports on its restoration and adds a further note (1965); see also Moir (1970).

3. Many of these are reproduced in the original Greek by K. Müller (1855). The parts of these *peripli* relating to Russia are given in their original language and in translation by Latyshev(1947, 1948, 1949). Other studies of them include Arkas(1853); Neumann(1844);.Paleolog(1853); Panagiodor-Nikovul(1848); Wagner(1885); and an untitled article in *Odesskoye Obshchestvo Istorii i Drevnostey, Zapiski* III(1853), 144-150.

4. These charts have been carefully described and investigated and there exists a rich literature about them. The most important works include: Wuttke(1870); Th. Fischer(1886); Ongania(1881); Wagner(1896); Wolkenhauer(1904); Steger(1896); Nordens-köld (1897); Kretschmer (1909); Stevenson (1911b) (Stevenson later published a number of facsimiles of sea-charts but they date from 1500);Uhden (1935); and Winter(1940). Many descriptions of map-collections have also been published. Of these, the most detailed list of Italian maps was compiled by Uzielli and Filippo (1882) but it is now already out of date.

5. The general history of South Russia is still being compiled. Its classical period is brilliantly described in the works of Rostovtsev(1918), (1922) and (1925). In English, there is the important work of Minns (1913). For a bibliography, see Rostovtsev(1925). Kulakovsky (1914) surveys the history of the Crimea and the adjoining steppe up to the 17th century. See also, Zagorsky (1922). Some other works on Italians in this area include Canale (1855); Heyd (1879); Bagrow (1956a); and Zouraeff (1966). Bagrow also refers to a number of articles by F. Brun which he published in *Imperatorskiy Novorossiyskiy Universitet, Odessa, Zapiski* and *Odesskoye obshchestvo Istorii i Drevnostey, Zapiski*; a selection of the more interesting of these articles dealing with the historical geography of the coasts of the Black Sea were later revised by the author and reprinted in two books, entitled *Chernomorye*, as supplements to the former periodical named above. The editor, however, has been unable to cite directly any of these articles, as Bagrow included no date in his reference.

6. The Dominican Julian visited, in 1235, the Hungarians of the Volga region. On his journey see Andreyevskiy (1863). In 1243, an Englishman in known to have travelled in these parts [Hakluyt(1903)I,50-54]. Also, there was Aszelini, Plano Carpini, Simon of Santa-Cantena (all in 1245); Rubruk (1253); Marco Polo (1271); Giovanni da Monte Corvino (1288); Gaiton (1290); Rinald de Monte Croix (1296); Oderico de Pordenoni (1317); John Mandeville (1332)!; Fr. Pegolotti (1335); Ibn Batuta (1347); Shiltbery (1394); etc.

7. See Potocki(1796) which refers to the maps of Vesconte (1318), Benincasa (1480), Fredutijs (1497), Agnese (1514) and two anonymous works - an atlas whose whereabouts is not indicated, and a map in the Wolfenbuetel Library. Potocki's work was translated into Russian by Spasskiy. Other works include Spasskiy(1846), Serristori (1856); Thomas (1864), and Brun. See also Nordenskiöld (1897); Kretschmer (1909) and Kulakovsky (1899a), (1899b) and (1914).

8. The original 1320 version (92x60), in Firenze, Biblioteca dell' di Stato, was first reproduced by Ongania (1881)T.III(5:2). It has also been reproduced by La Roncière (1924) T.VI(5:2); Yusuf Kamal (1936) IV, Part I,1138(1:1); Bagrow (1964) PL.XXXIII(9:2); and Nordenskiöld (1897) Pl.V(5:2). According to Bagrow the original was destroyed in 1943.

9. Wieser (1912), in comparing the world map with that of A. de Virga, concludes that the Atlas should be ascribed to the beginning of the 15th century or not earlier that the last quarter of the 14th century. This opinion, however, is convincingly challenged by Kimble (1935). The Medici Atlas is preserved in the Biblioteca Laurentiana, Firenze. It has been reproduced completely only by Ongania (1881). Nordenskiöld (1897) T.X.(36x27) reproduces part of Western Europe and the Adriatic and Caspian Seas (3:2). The world map has been reproduced by Wieser (1912)10-11(47x36).

10. The maps have been reproduced or described by:
    1) Winter (1940) who ascribes it to Angelo Dalorto; it is (107x66);
    2) Magnaghi (1898) (1:1) (i.e. 66x107) and (1899) without the map. A reproduction (1:1) in color on four sheets by Hinks (1929); and Yusuf Kamal (1937) IV, Part II,1197(8:7); the reproductions by Hinks and Yusuf Kamal both bear the date 1325;
    3) Nordenskiöld(1897)T.VIII and IX(9:7) from the original (104x75) in the possession of Mr. A Lesouëf, Paris; Hamy (1886) without the map and (1903) an excellent reproduction (1:1); and Yusuf Kamal (1937) IV, Part II,1222(6:5);

4) Described in detail, with the entire text, by Buchon and Tastu (1839); first reproduced completely by Santarem (1849) I,Pl. 32-33(1:1) (196x62); then in Choix de documents (1883) T.III; Nordenskiöld (1897) T.XI-XIV(7:6) from Choix de documents (1883); Yusuf Kamal (1938) IV, Part III,1303(1:1) who ascribes this map to Cresques; and Bagrow(1912a) 24,#14(incomplete) and (1964) Pl.XXXVII-XXXIX(4:1) who also ascribes it to Cresques. See also Hamy (1891);

5) LaRoncière (1924) T.XIII (Spain and North Africa only); the Baltic is reproduced in Bjornbo and Petersen(1908);

6) Marcel(1896) T.III in 6 sheets (each 31x41);

7) Described in Turkish with a rather unsuccessful reproduction by Hakki(1936) 137-193.

8) Reproduced photographically by Ongania(1881) T.XVI; described by Th. Fischer(1886)213-218;

9) This map 115 dia.) is reproduced by Kretschmer (1897) T.IV with a colored hand drawn reproduction(3:2) and in reprint (1968) (7:2); Longhèna and Pulle (1907) (16.5 dia.) and (1908); a reproduction in color by Kimble (1934) (1:1); Bagrow (1964) Pl.XLIII(6:1); and Almagià and Destombes(1964) Pl.XXXIII(7:2).

10) A fragment of a circular Catalan map was found in the Topkapu Sarayi Kütübhane, Istanbul. Its description and reproduction are given by Hakki(1936)193-240.

11) Pizzigano's map (131x85) has been reproduced by Jomard(1842-62) Pl.X.2 and X.3 (a lithograph) and by Yusuf Kamal (1937) IV,Part II,1286(1:1) from a manuscript copy of 1827.

11. Three manuscript copies of this description are known to be extant — all three were made in the last third of the 15th century. They were initially published by La Espada (1877); the English translation can be found in Markham (1912).

12. It is necessary to survey the information on areas beyond these mountains (Urals), as they are, for the most parts, legendary. The Far East region is described and analyzed by Hallberg(1906).

13. Brun gives reproductions of part of Pizzigano's map of 1367 and of the Catalan map of 1375. He also tries to identify each place-name with the name of a Khan who is known to have been stationed along the Volga. In some cases, such as Uvek, this approach has not been entirely satisfactory.

CHAPTER 4: RUSSIA OF THE LATE MIDDLE AGES

14. For a long time, it was believed that the maps had also been compiled by Sanuto. But when a manuscript copy of *Liber Secretorum* was found bearing the signature of Petrus Vesconte and the date of 1320, the authorship of the maps was attributed to Vesconte. In fact, Sanuto is not known to have produced any maps himself.

Altogether, about twenty manuscript examples of Marino Sanuto are known but not all of them contain maps, or in particular the world map. The most important of these manuscripts are preserved in the Biblioteca Medicea Laurenziana, Firenze; The British Museum, London; the Bibliothèque Nationale, Paris; Biblioteca Apostolica Vaticana, Roma; and Bibliothèque Royale de Belgique, Bruxelles.

The world map (34 dia.) was first published by Bongars(1611) from which it has been reproduced by Yusuf Kamal(1936)IV,Part 1,1175(1:1) and Bagrow(1964)Pl.XXXV(2:1) and hand copied by Nordenskiöld(1889)51(3:2). Two examples in the Biblioteca Apostolica Vaticana (Codices 2977(28 dia.) and 1362(27 dia.) — the latter bearing Vesconte's signature) are reproduced by Yusuf Kamal(1936)IV,Part I,1169(1:1)and(1936)IV,Part I,1160(1:1); a defective hand drawn copy of the latter is in Kretschmer(1891a)T.8(1:1) and, from Kretschmer, by Nordenskiöld(1897)17(3:2). The Paris Example is reprinted in Almagià and Destombes(1964)Pl.XVI(7:4). A copy in the British Museum is reproduced by Almagià(1944)I,22(5:4).

A map of the Black Sea(19x18) from a 1318 portolan atlas by Vesconte in the Österreichische Nationalbibliothek, Wien, is reproduced by Nordenskiöld(1897)Pl.VI(7:5); an example(30x22) from Codex Vaticanus #2972 has been hand copied by Kretschmer(1891a)T.9(1:1), andhis copy is reproduced in Nordenskiöld(1897)33(4:3). An example (45x28) from Codex Vaticanus #1362 is reproduced by Almagià(1944)I,T.IV(5:3).

On Sanuto and Vesconte, see Kretschmer(1891a), Simonsfield(1881), Dessimoni(1893), and Magnocavallo(1902) and (1903).

15. Vesconte might have obtained a great deal of information on the southern Baltic coast from Marino Sanuto. See Spekke(1948)43.

16. This description has been edited with the map from Kretschmer(1891a) at hand — here there are two rivers, while in the original there are four to the east of the Dnepr. An additional source of variance is the fact that this map (as are all reproductions published by Kretschner) is not a photograph but a hand-drawn copy.

17. Paolino is also known by the name Paulinus Minorita, Paulinus de Venetiis, Paulin de Pouzzoles, Poulinus, or Jordanus. He died in the year 1345. His manuscripts can be found in the Biblioteca Apostolica, Roma, (24 dia.) and the Bibliothèque Nationale, Paris, (33 dia.): the world maps from both manuscripts are each reproduced in Yusuf Kamal(1936)IV,Part I,1172(1:1) and (1936)IV,PartI,1174(1:1). The world map from the Vatican manuscript has been reproduced by Almagià(1944)I,T.I.(1:1). The world map from theParis manuscript has also been reproduced in Santarem(1849)I,Pls.28,29,30 and Nordenskiöld(1897)57(9:5) from Santarem.

18. On maps of the Caspian by Vesconte and other Italian cartographers see Bagrow(1956a).

19. The manuscript of this *Cosmography* is preserved at the Biblioteca Apostolica Vaticana, Archivio alla Sacristia di San Pietro, in Cod.Lat.H.31. The map (28x19) has been reproduced by Yusuf Kamal(1938)IV,Part III, on the cover (1:1) and on the verso of p.1376(1:1); Bagrow(1964)Pl.XLI(5:4); and Almagià and Destombes(1964)Pl.XXII(5:4). The manuscript is undated but it is bound together with another one which is dated 1414. Judging from the shape of Scandinavia, Mela's map should, however, be attributed to a later period.

20. A very good photo-reproduction(1:1) is in Wieser(1912)Pl.I (overall—68x43; 41 dia.); also in Yusuf Kamal(1938)IV,Part III,1377(1:1), and Almagià and Destombes(1964)Pl.XXVIII(2:1).

21. Bianco's atlas is preserved in the Biblioteca Marciana, Venezia. His world map (25 dia.) was first reproduced by Formaleoni(1788)(1:1). Reproductions are also in Santarem(1850)II,Pl.38(1:1); Nordenskiöld(1897)19(1:1) from Formaleoni; Peschel(1869)(5:4); and Skelton, et al(1965)Pl.VI(1:1).

22. This map (42 dia.) of map itself) is preserved in the Biblioteca Apostolica Vaticana, Roma: Cod. Palat. Lat. 1362b (where Kretschmer discovered the maps of Vesconte). Kretschmer(1891b)T.10(1:1) appends a colored lithographic reproduction which, unfortunately, is not quite exact because it is a hand-drawn copy. Reproductions can be found in Almagià and Destombes(1964)Pl.XXXI(7:2) and Almagià(1944)I,T.XII(3:2).

23. Map of 1442 (27.5 dia.): described and reproduced in color by Crivellari(1903)T.1(1:1); Manzi(1900)(9:8). Map of 1448 (28 dia.): described and reproduced by Santarem(1850)II,Pl.49(1:1); Durazzo(1885)(5:2); Longhena(1929)(5:2) in color; and Nordenskiöld(1897)61(4:3) from Santarem.

    Map of 1452-53 (59 dia.): first described and reproduced by Berchet(1880)(1:1); Ongania(1881)Pl.XIV(1:1); Wright(1928)(1:1); Durazzo(1885)(5:1); Molmenti(1927)(7:1); and Almagià and Destombes(1964)Pl.XXX(5:1).

24. The map, evidently meant to be a decorative wall-piece, originally consisted of two iron plates on which a world map was engraved.It was found in 1794 in an antiquarian's shop and acquired by Cardinal Borgia for his museum at Valletzi. In 1797, the Cardinal's nephew ordered a full-sized copper-engraving of the map (63 dia.), from which all later reproductions have been made. Thus, there are no direct reproductions of the original. A lithograph can be found in Santarem(1849)Pl.23(1:1); a photograph in Nordenskiöld(1891)(8:7); a hand copy in Seroux d'Agincourt(1823)T.XL(7:2); Bagrow(1964)71(4:1); Almagià(1944)I,T.XI(7:3); and Almagià and Destombes(1964)Pl.XXIX(9:5).

25. The map(81x42) is preserved in Firenze, Biblioteca Nazionale Centrale. Its most exhaustive description is that by Wuttke(1870) which includes a schematic representation. A photo-reproduction is given in Ongania(1881)Pl.X(5:4); it is described by Th. Fischer(1886)155-206; a photographic black and white reproduction is found in Stevenson(1912) frontispiece(9:2); in color in Bagrow(1964)Pl.D(7:2); and in Almagià and Destombes(1964)Pl.XXXIV(7:3). There is a considerable literature on the question of the map's authorship. See Crinò(1941); Winter(1942); and Biasutti(1941).

26. This map 196 cm. in diameter) was found in the Camaldolese monastery in the island of Murano, Venezia. It is now preserved in the Biblioteca Marciana, Venezia. Reproductions are included in Santarem(1850)II,43-48(1:1); Ongania(1881)Pl.XV(3:1); Pullé(1901)T.3(4:1); Zurla(1806)(7:1); and Bagrow(1964)Pl.XLII(11:1). Photographs of the map, either on one sheet (11:1) or on four sheets are sold in Venezia. A coloured reproduction was published at Firenze in 1941 by Alinari; Gasparrini-Leporace(1956) also reproduced it in color. The portion of the map representing South Russia was reprinted from Santarem in Materialy(1871); in Bagrow(1912a)26, and in Winter(1962)23. Larger portions of Russia are reproduced in Almagià and Destombes(1964)Pl.XXXV(6:1); and Almagià(1944)I,T.XIII-XV. Besides Zurla, the map has been studied by Vincent(1807)II,661-679 and (1808)115-218; and Bagrow(1956a).

27. The reading of these and other place-names given here may possibly be incorrect. Bagrow apparently studied the reproduction of Fra Mauro's map in Santarem which is not a photograph but a lithograph. Its spellings are a function of the copyist's familiarity with medieval writing, and many are apparently not clear. The editor was unable to examine a clearer reproduction.

    Hallberg(1906) examines names from all over Siberia and Central Asia including the Trans-Volga. His statements, however, should not be accepted uncritically because his work was gathered, for the most part, from re-editions of early descriptions of expeditions and Hallberg evidently did not verify the data provided by these materials. In dealing with Fra Mauro's material he was guided by Zurla's interpretation (1806) which was already out of date. Moreover, Zurla has not collated his materials with Russian sources as these sources were unknown to him.

CHAPTER 5: EXTINCTION OF MEDIEVAL INFLUENCES

28. Reproductions of these maps are given in Santarem(1842-53) and Nordenskiöld(1889)38 and T.XXXI.

29. a) Codex Vat. Gr. 177 in the Biblioteca Apostolica Vaticana, Roma, and
    b) an imperfect manuscript in the Vatopedi Monastery on Mount Athos. It has been reproduced by Langlois(1867). Its world map is now in the British Museum, London Add. 19391 and has been reproduced by Fischer(1916b)T.II.

30. As a result, a number of experimental attempts were made to improve on the originals. None of them succeeded for the same reason that hindered the oroginal mapmaker — many of the geographical points are given only as relative positions. These attempts include: Kulakovsky(1899a) and (1899b); Latýshev(1899) and (1900); Braun(1899); and Borisov(1908-1911). Perhaps we will see some contemporary solutions using the computer.

31. Brun locates this place on the Ingulets. The author [(1945)377] raises the question of its association with present-day Kherson, or to be exact, with Alyeshki lying opposite this city (Oleshje in the Chronicles).

32. We have mentioned the approximate way in which certain features have been located by the text of the *Geographia*; here is a good example: "the Amadoc mountains 55°-51°", i.e. only one geographical coordinate (latitude) is given. As a result the compiler of the map in Verson A took the liberty of draughting a whole system of mountain ridges combining the Tevca-Amodoci-Bodinvs mountains. Kulakovsky, referred to in a previous footnote, drew mountains east of the Borysthenes; Latyshev, objecting to the separation of the Amadoka mountains from Lake Amadoka by the Borysthenes, drew the mountains west of the river.

33. This conclusion is challenged by Buczek[(1966)17] who has studied both Ptolemy's European Sarmatia and Greater Germania. He states that "the description and the maps in the *Geography*...were consistent with the actual conditions in this part of Europe in the first and at the beginning of the second centuries."

34. Some details and maps are given in Herz(1870). Kulakovsky(1899a) appends "A map of the Crimea after Ptolemy".

35. This manuscript is preserved in the Bibliothèque Municipale, Nancy, France. It is described in Blau (1835). The map(22x15) has been reproduced by Nordenskiöld(1889)49(1:1) and Bagrow(1964)78(5:3) among others.

36. According to Dahlgren's interpretation [Nordenskiöld(1889)54], Roderin is Roden or Roslagen. But in later maps Roderin is situated so near the Neva (e.g., in Waldseemüller's 1516 map it lies east of Výborg) that Dahlgren's interpretation seems doubtful. This question is discussed further in p. 112.

    The map(57x31) is reproduced by Nordenskiöld(1889)T.XXX(1:1); he also reproduced, on page 61, the maps from Codex Zamoysky, 1468(5:1), Codex Bruxelles(6:1), and the 1482 Ulm edition of the *Geographia*(5:1).

37. The Italian version was printed by Nicolo Todescho whose identity with Nicolaus Germanus is still unsolved. This edition is undated although several dates are suggested: 1478 by Nordenskiöld[(1889)12-14]; and 1482 by J. Fischer[(1932)375-398]; i.e., a few years after the compilation of the two Italian manuscripts.

38. A discussion of the reasons for attributing these maps to Nicolaus Cusanus can be found in Bagrow(1930)29-33 and (1964)147.

    The original of Martellus' map (57x41) is in the Biblioteca Nazionale Centrale, Firenze. A photograph is given in Fischer(1930)(5:4). A less distinct photocopy of this reproduction is given in Herrmann(1940)T.1.

    Another manuscript map ascribed to Nicolaus Cusanus is preserved in the University Library, Leiden. It is however, still poorer in detail. It is also reproduced by Hermann from a reproduction by Wolkenhauer. There is some question as to the accuracy of the latter's reproduction because of very obvious mistakes that can be seen in the toponymy, e.g., "Rissei montes" instead of Riffei montes, etc.

39. The question of its authorship and production is considered by Bagrow(1964)147. Examples of this map are to be found in the British museum; Bibliothèque Nationale (on parchment); Thrüringische Landesbibliothek, Weimar; Germanisches National-Museum, Nüremberg; Deutsshe Staatsbibliothek, East Berlin; and the Bayerische Armeebibliothek, München. The last-mentioned example is the earliest because it was impressed from the planche before the uppermost line has been cut off. The map's overall size, without the title, is approximately(52x36). A very poor reproduction in phototype is given in Herrman(1940)T.3/4. Reproductions of other examples include: S. Ruge(1891)(7:5); Tooley(1952)Pl.20(3:1); Nordenskiöld(1897)T.XXXV(9:7)[all of these from the London example]; Metelka(1895)20(1:1)[Weimar example]; Henne-an-Rhyn(1903)I,420(10:9)[the Nüremberg example]; Buczek(1966)Pl.3(5:3); Bagrow(1964)Pl.LXXII(5:2). The London and Müchen engravings contain information below the southern limit of the trapezoidal frame.

    Buczek(1966), mentioned above, has appeared in both a Polish (1963) and a revised English version (1966). References hare to plates and pages will be to the English edition with a larger collection of plates(60 vs. 48 for the Polish edition); unfortunately for those with access only to the Polish edition, these reference numbers are rarely the same.

40. An exact copy of the contents of this map, but for a few misprints, is the map of Giovanni Andrea Vavassore. Although previously known only by name, this map was discovered before World War II in the Kartensammlung des hiesigen Geographischen Institut, Göttingen. However, it was apparently destroyed during the war. On the author and his maps see

Bagrow(1936b). The map(52x37) has been reproduced by Herrmann(1940)T.6; and Buczek(1966)T.4(9:5). The map, a crude woodcut, has been transformed from the trapezoidal projection to a rectangular format.

41. Münzer's map (60x40) is better known as the map from Schedel's *Liber Chronicarum, Nüremberg*, 1493; his authorship has only recently been established. See J. Fischer(1918). On the geographical contents of Schedel and a reproduction of the map see Schultheiss(1894)8-9(7:4). The map is also reproduced by Nordenskiöld(1889)9(5:2); Herrmann(1940)T.5; Materiałỳ(1871); and Bagrow(1964)Pl.LXXIII(3:1). On Mnzer himself, see Goldschmidt(1938).

42. On Beneventanus, see Birkenmajer(1901). The 1507 map (52x38) has been reproduced by Kordt(1910)T.XIX(1:1); Chowaniec(1955)59(2:1); and by Nordenskiöld(1889)25(5:2). The 1513 map(55x41) has been reproduced by Kordt(1899)25(5:2). The 1513 map (55x41) has been reproduced by Kordt(1899)T.II(1:1) and Chowaniec(1955)60(7:2). As indicated by its title, the 1507 map embraces all of Germany, whereas that of 1513 is limited in the west by the Oder and in the south by the Danube. The toponymy of the lower course of the Dnepr and the coasts of the Black Sea is borrowed from Genoese maps of the 14th-16th centuries. The description of the map in the text below is from the 1513 edition unless otherwise noted.

43. This map (approx. 232x128) survives as a proof sheet in the library of Prince Waldburg-Wolfegg at the Schloss Wolfegg, Württemberg. Its title: VNIVERSALIS COSMOGRAPHIA SECVNDVM PTHOLOMAI TRADITIONEM ET AMERICI VES-PVCII ALIORVQVE L'VSTRATIONES. It is discussed in detail by Fischer and Wieser(1903) who reproduce it in 12 sheets(1:1) and on one sheet(4:1). It is also reproduced by Bragow(1964)Pl.LXI(12:1) and that portion of the map relating to Russia in (1962)33(6:5). On Waldseemüller, see Bagrow(1932)97-104.

44. The surviving copy (approximately 223x123) is also a proof sheet preserved in the Schloss Wolfegg, Württemberg. Its rather lengthy title begins: "CARTA MARINA NAVIGATORIA PORTVGALLEN NAVIGATIONES ATOVE TOCIVS COG-NITORBIS TERRE MARIS NOSTRIS TEMPORIBVS..."

It has been reproduced by Fischer and Wieser(1903) in 12 sheets (1:1) and on one sheet (4:1) and by Bagrow(1964)Pl.LXII(11:1). Portions of the map dealing with Russia have been reproduced by Bagrow(1962)34(1:1) and Kordt(1906)Pl.1.

45. The book, *Tractatus de duabus Sarmatiis Asiana et Europiana et de Contentis in eis*, Cracovie, 1517, was repeatedly republished and also translated. On Matthew's work see Zamỳslovskiy(1880b)71-75; Michow(1885); and Wojciechowski(1926).

46. On Münster's correspondence with Laski and on the materials he received from Poland, see Buczek(1935).

47. This sketch was published by Münster(1588)48. Here, on p. 181, he recorded that he obtained the information from Matthew of Miechów "qui ex professo nostro aevo de his regionibus et flumnibus scripsit, et nos quoque supra in Solino cap. 25 expresimus per figuram origines et confluentias me oratorum atque aliorum fluviorum". The first to annotate and publish this map was Nordenskiöld(1885)262 and (1889)108(1:1). Other reproductions accompanied by text are found in Anuchin(1895)84; Michow(1906)12-15,T.1(1:1); Kordt(1889)T.9(1:1); and Bagrow(1964)172(9:5).

PART III: THE 16TH CENTURY —

RUSSIA COMING INTO FOCUS

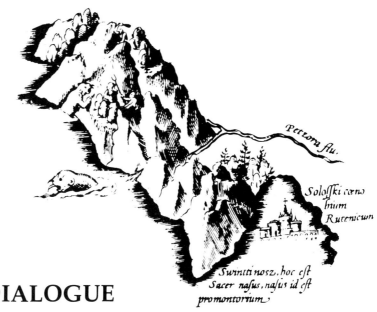

CHAPTER 6:

THE BEGINNING OF A DIALOGUE

The next period of the development of the cartography of Russia is connected with the names of foreigners who had visited Russia, and of Russians who had travelled in Western Europe. Materials or accounts exported from Russia doubtless circulated among European cartographers, influencing their work, before they were finally published. But it is difficult to trace the origins of these materials, and how they were used, as they were frequently elaborated upon and supplemented with information from sources unknown to us. Thus, on this basis, it is difficult to establish the chronology of maps produced in this period — other factors must be considered.

The most important figures of this period, in chronological order, were: Sigismund Herberstein, who visited Russia in 1517 and 1526; Dmitriy Gerasimov, the head of a Russian Embassy to Roma in 1525; and Ivan Lyatsky, who fled from Russia in 1534. However, the intervals and time between the gathering of their information and the publication of their maps disturbs this order:

> Lyatsky's map — made by Wied in 1542; published by Münster in 1544; and published by Wied himself in 1555.

> Herberstein's map — produced before 1546; engraved by Augustin Hirsvogel in 1546.

> Gerasimov's map — drawn perhaps as early as 1525; redrawn and published in MS by Battista Agnese c. 1550.

While Herberstein had visited Russia before 1525, his information was not utilized until much later; we do not know exactly when he produced his map. Lyatsky fled from Russia in 1534 and could thus have given his materials to Münster only after this date, and even then he communicated them through Wied, who answered the appeal made by Münster (1536) in publishing the first edition of his *Cosmographia*. Therefore, let us begin our survey with Gerasimov, who by some means or other provided P. Giovio with information on Russia in 1525.

Dmitriy Gerasimov

In this year, an Embassy from Grand Duke Vasiliy III Ivanovich visited Roma. It brought a letter and gifts to Pope Clement VII. The pope attached to this Embassy the well-known historian and physician Paolo Giovio (Paulus Jovius) entrusting him with the task of obtaining from it as much information as possible on Muscovy and recording it in a book. The Embassy was headed by Dmitriy Gerasimov[1], who was born about 1465 and died after 1535. As a child he had lived in Livonia and learned there the German and Latin languages; later he was engaged in the *Posol'sky dvor* (Diplomatic Service) and served in embassies to Sweden, Denmark, Prussia, and Vienna. He stayed for two consecutive years at Roma and Firenze and there met many European scholars. His main interest was religion, and he (together with the other interpreter attached to the *Posol'sky dvor*, Vasiliy Vlasiy is known to have helped Maxim the Greek to translate the *Tolkovaya Psaltyr'* [a Psalter with explanitory notes or rubrics]. He also translated and edited a number of other similar works. Gerasimov enjoyed the well-deserved reputation of a learned man, whose judgment could be trusted and respected.

Giovio did not waste any time in gathering copious material from his conversations with Gerasimov during the Embassy's stay at Roma in June and July, 1525. That same year Giovio published the results of his investigation(1525).[2] Although Giovio refers at the beginning of his work to a map of Muscovy printed simultaneously with the book, there is no map in either edition of his *Libellus*. A map connected with Gerasimov's name was, however, found at a later date; namely a manuscript map of Russia included in some of the atlases of the well-known Venetian cartographer Battista Agnese.[3]

H. Michow was the first to pay attention to this map (Figures 20 and 21) of which the Venetian manuscript bears the title: "Moscoviae tabula relatione dimetrii legati descrypta sicuti ipse a pluribus accepit, cum totum provincium minime peragrasse fateatur, anno MDXXV octobris".[4] The October date indicates that the map was made after Gerasimov had left Roma. It is difficult to establish why the map was not engraved and appended to the book, but the explanation proposed by Michow, namely, that this was due to a lack of wood-engravers in Italy, seems insufficient. Map-printing was adequately developed in Italy at that time; we have but to recall the four different editions of Ptolemy's *Geographia* — two of them containing *tabulae modernae* — printed before 1525. Moreover, so prominent a cartographer and engraver as G.A. Vavassore had already started his activities (his first dated map is of 1522).

Then, why should not Gerasimov's map have been engraved in Italy, if not as a woodcut, as a copper-engraving? This may be explained by presuming that Gerasimov had no part in compiling this map, but that it was prepared at a later date from Giovio's text. Giovio might even have made it himself. As Gerasimov enjoyed the Russian Duke's full confidence, he would scarcely have betrayed it by drawing a map of Russia abroad for the use of foreigners, since he knew that all maps were kept strictly secret by the government.[5] Ramusio informs us that a Russian at Augsburg showed one of the local scientists a map, in order to prove that India could be reached via the Ice Ocean. This Russian might have been Gerasimov, who passed through Augsburg on his way to and from Roma. In 1525, Vasiliy Vlasiy also travelled through Augsburg accompanying Prince I. Ya. Zasekin to Spain. There is, however, no indication whether this map showed by "the Russian" was of Russian or of European workmanship. Finally, a Russian might have given a drawing of some kind, even one which was quite wrong, in an attempt to get rid of a tiresome petitioner.[6]

Giovio might, of course, have shown Gerasimov sketches of different regions as he prepared them according to his notes. However, we do not even know whether Gerasimov was aware that Giovio was recording information from their discussions with a view to writing a book. It is very possible that he knew nothing about it. We may also suppose that after having drawn the map from the text he had compiled, Giovio nevertheless doubted its accuracy and did not venture to have it engraved.

Michow carried out a meticulous comparison of the map with the text and found no significant divergencies. However, an examination of Agnese's map raises the question of whether it was compiled or even approved by Gerasimov. This does not mean that Michow's comparative study was not thorough enough; he looked only for divergencies and he found none. It is striking, however, to find a number of details included in the map which are not mentioned or are only slightly mentioned in the text. For example, in the northwest, the text mentions the [Severnaya] Dvina and its tributary the Yuga (Yug?), the town of Ustyug at their confluence, and describes the various tribes of North Russia who pay tribute to Moskva in Ustyug. The map, on the other hand, shows the "Yugra" (or Migra, i.e., the Megra which flows into Onezheskoye Ozero) as the westernmost river flowing into "Oceanus Siticus". Further to the east, and also flowing into the Oceanus Siticus, is the "Pecerra" (the Pechora or the Pechenga?) and then a nameless river (in the text the "Dividna") with two left bank tributaries (from the west) and three right bank tributaries from the east, four of which have their sources in lakes. Only one of the affluents — the middle one to the east — is named; the Sukhona (no such name appears in the text). The town Istiuga is situated at the confluence of the two most southerly right and left bank tributaries. Gerasimov, having descended the Sukhona and the Severnaya Dvina on his embassy to Norway, via the Ice Ocean and around the North Cape, must have been familiar with these northern rivers.[7] But he could scarcely have admitted such crude errors as locating the Pechora (unless the Pechenga is meant here) west of the Dvina, or of placing the Yug northwest of the Sukhona. The map, in fact, is much richer in names than is the text.

This raises the question of the origin of the additional information which appears on the map. Assuming that the map found in several of Agnese's atlases is a copy of Giovio's original sketch, several possibilities exist: 1) Giovio might have gathered them from Gerasimov but failed to record them in his text; or 2) he obtained them from some other source; or 3) they could have been included by Gerasimov himself. The last seems improbable because Gerasimov knew Latin well and could easily have transcribed the names from the Russian so no inconsistencies in spelling would appear from the text to the map. The first possibility also seems unlikely. Thus, there evidently existed some other source. But, a fourth possibility exists — that Agnese could have added them himself. This possibility is supported by the fact that a number of towns and rivers indicated in the map are named, and that some of the names given on the map, but not found in the text, are quite changed. The changes could be ascribed to a copyists's misunderstanding or unfamiliarity with the material, and therefore something we could not ascribe to Giovio.

As to a source that might have been available to

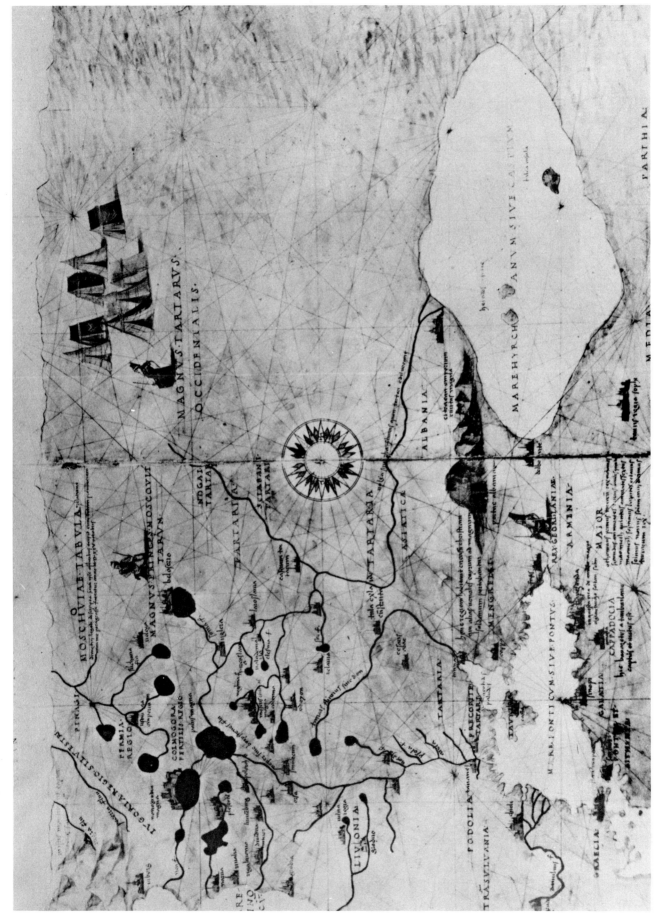

FIGURE 20. Gerasimov's map of Russia, 1525, from a MS. atlas by Battista Agnese. Reduced in scale (4:3).

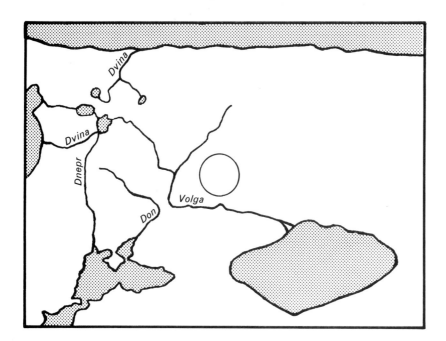

FIGURE 21. Simplified sketch of Gerasimov's map showing the five great rivers of European Russia, the Baltic, Black and Caspian Seas, and the northern ocean. Many of the maps that follow will be presented in this standardized style and orientation to facilitiate a comparison of the progressive changes which took place in the map of Russia.

either Giovio or Agnese, we know of another map, very similar to Agnese's, which was inserted by Jacopo Gastaldi in his edition of Ptolemy's *Geographia*, Venezia, 1548. The map, "MOSCOVIA NOVA TABVLA",[8] is a small (17x13) copper-engraving. Bagrow [(1962)42-43] compares this map in some detail with that of Agnese, and concludes that no direct relationship can be seen between the two maps, although it is clear that they stem from a common prototype (presumably Giovio's original map). Gastaldi makes no reference to it; Agnese indicates the original source material, i.e. "the information obtained from Gerasimov which he had heard of from Giovio". Bagrow further concludes that the information introduced into Giovio's map by Gastaldi was borrowed from Italian sources, such as the Genoese and Venetian sea-charts. Since these influences are not seen in Agnese's map, we can assume Gastaldi's map had no influence upon it.

Ivan Lyatsky

The next contribution to Western Europe's knowledge of Russia was made by a fugitive Russian boyar, the *Okol'nitchiy* Ivan Lyatsky. Lyatsky, an emigrant from Lithuania, spent the first half of his life in Moskva serving in administrative and military posts in different parts of the country. Thus, he was better

informed than Gerasimov on many parts of Russia. In 1534, a year after the death of Tsar Vasiliy III, Lyatsky joined the party of Prince Mikhail Glinsky, an uncle of the dowager Tsarina Helen who ruled the country in the name of her infant son, the future Ivan IV. When ancient feuds between princely and boyar families broke out, many of the nobility, among them Mikhail Glinsky, were arrested. Lyatsky fled to Lithuania and settled down at Vilna [Vil'nyus].

Somehow, it became known in Danzig that Lyatsky could provide rich descriptive material on Muscovy. Hearing this, the Senator Johann Koppe took the first opportunity to go to Vilna, taking with him Anton Wied, an artist whom he had persuaded to draw a map of Muscovy. Wied met Lyatsky and obtained from him the necessary material.[9] In the same year, 1542, Wied prepared the manuscript of his map; being an artist, he embellished it with drawings of hunting scenes and the various wild beasts populating the Russian forests. Whether Lyatsky had helped him with these drawings we do not know, but it can be said that they are executed not only with artistry, but also with some realism, which suggests that he may have done so. Proof of this assumption seems to be found in a series of inscriptions on the map, executed in Russian with calligraphic perfection. Wied scarcely knew Russian well enough for this.

Wied's map, drawn in 1542, remained for some time as a manuscript; nevertheless it became known to a number of persons. Among them was Herbers-

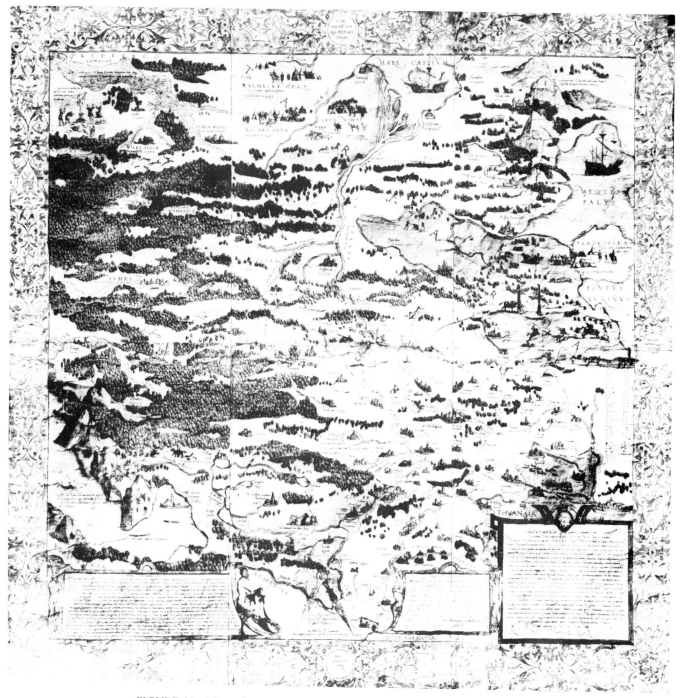

FIGURE 22. Map of Russia by Anton Wied, 1542, greatly reduced (5:1).

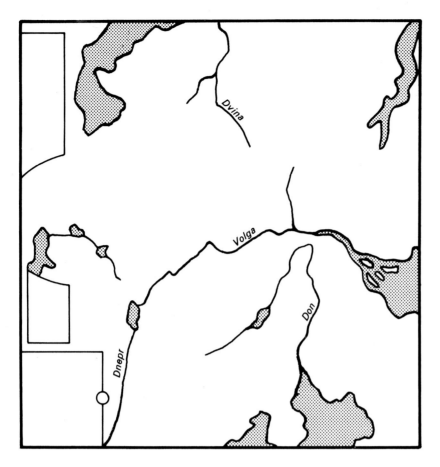

FIGURE 23. Sketch of Wied's 1542 map. Note change in orientation from Figure 22.

tein, to whom Wied might even have sent a copy at Lyatsky's suggestion. Reference to it is found in Gessner[(1548)111c,113b]; who later borrowed from Wied's map the scene of a moufflon hunt for his *Historiae Animalium*(1551). Still earlier, Wied had answered Münster's public appeal for geographic material for his *Cosmographia*. In his 1544 edition, Münster credits Wied (who was assisted by "...Johannes Jatski") with supplying him with materials on Muscovy, which apparently included text and a map. Thus Wied's map, even in this reduced and slightly simplified form, was given considerable circulation.

Wied's map (Figures 22 and 23) comprising six sheets, has no special title. There appears, in the lower right hand corner, a dedication to "Coppe" from A. Wied which explains what the map represents and that Lyatsky had assisted in its compilation. It also mentions Herberstein's request for a map, earlier, at Moskva, and that the request is now granted. This dedication is signed "Wilda...April Anno 1555." Immediately to the left of the dedication is another box containing the title "An'tony Wed do chtitelyu" (Anthony Wied to the reader). There follow a few instructions, in old Polonized Russian, on the use of the map and the date 1542 (but stated in the old

Slavonic calendar). Finally, in the lower left-hand corner, there is a short description of Muscovy also dated "Wilda...anno 1555..." The reason for the several dates is not clear. The earliest, 1542, probably refers to the production of the manuscript in Vilna with the aid of Lyatsky, while the dates April and November, 1555 presumably indicate the beginning and end of the engraving process.[10]

Who engraved and printed the map is unknown. The privilege of publishing the map had been granted by Emperor Charles V, of the Holy Roman Empire, although the names within the margin — Oost, Zuydt — indicate a Dutch origin. In any case, the engraving is of high artistic value, and represents the first map to be printed in the Russian language. All of the geographical names are given not only in Latin, but also in Russian; only the legends referring to the hunting scenes and animals are not repeated in Russian. A special column on the right-hand side gives the two alphabets: Russian and Latin. It is curious that while many of the names given in Latin are Polonized — Schmolentz, Dzwina, Wollodzea, etc. — those in Russian are given their authentic pronunciation.

The author has previously described[(1962)45] the contents of this map. Among the notable features

FIGURE 24.   Wied's map of Russia as engraved by F. Hogenberg, 1570. Half-scale here (2:1). Courtesy The British Library Board.

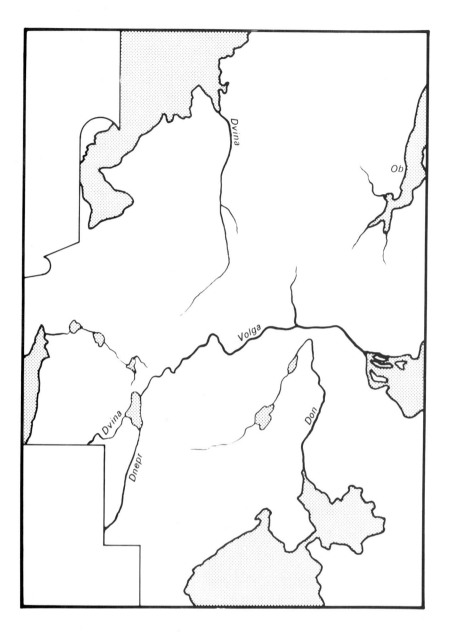

FIGURE 25. Hogenberg' copy of Wied's map in simplified form.

of this map is the absence of any high mountains, with the exception of those on the coast of the Beloye More, between Solovki and the Sev. Dvina. Some small hills are indicated in the north-eastern corner of the map, i.e. in the Urals region, but these are easily overlooked. It is characteristic that the whole of northern Russia is covered with woods, while in southern Russia they are all but absent.

Later, a copper-engraving of this map was produced by F. Hogenberg (Figure 24 and 25) who signed it (in the upper left-hand corner) "Franciscus Hogenb: ex vero Sculpsit 1570". All of the Russian names and legends are omitted although the two dates 1555 have been preserved.[11] While Wied's original manuscript is nearly square in shape, Hogenberg's map is oblong, to suit the format of an atlas. To do this, Hogen-

berg widened the map-frame in the north and the south. In the north, this necessitated supplementing the Wied-Lyatsky data by introducing the lower course of the Mezen'; the village of Strupili castrum, and the upper courses of the Petzara (the Pechora?), Berezwa and Sossa Rivers. It is difficult to construct the source from which Hogenberg obtained these data. Strupili castrum appears only in one of Mercator's maps, namely that of Europe 1572; the Berezwa and Sossa appear only in a much later map of Russia, 1594, by Mercator. No other possible cartographic sources have been discovered as yet. Perhaps it was borrowed from Herberstein's description of the routes leading to the Ob'; Herberstein, in his turn, had borrowed it from the Russian itinerary which he reprinted in his work on Muscovy. Besides a few

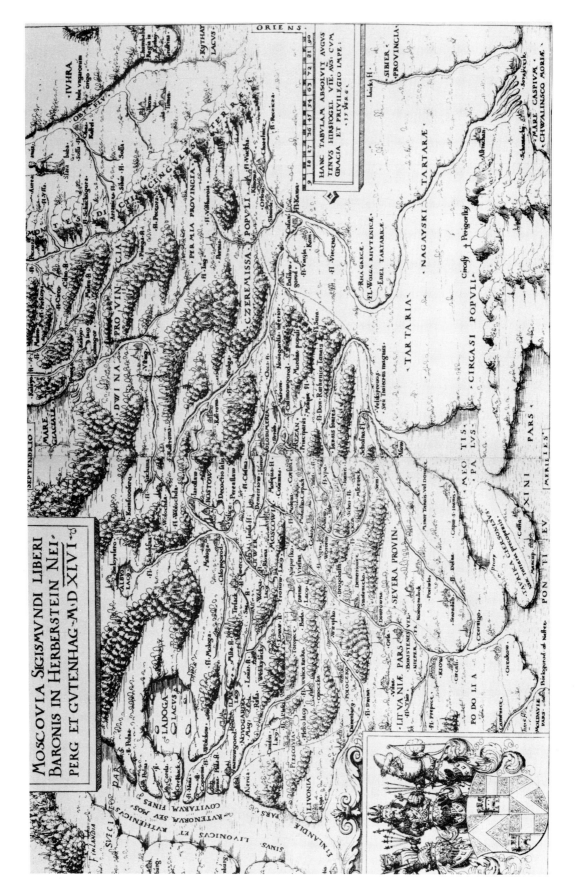

FIGURE 26. Map of Russia by Herberstein as engraved by A. Hirschvogel, 1546, (7:3). Courtesy The British Library Board.

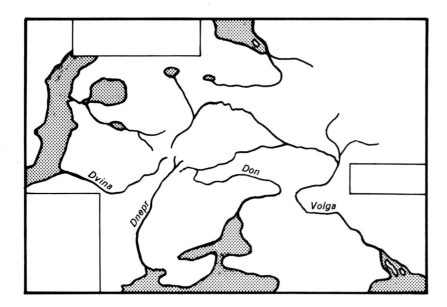

FIGURE 27.   Sketch of Herberstein's 1546 map.

inaccuracies in the names copied from Wied's original manuscript and a few insignificant omissions, Hogenberg's map does not show any other divergencies from it.

Wied's map was not begotten on a lucky day — neither the original nor Hogenberg's copy gained much attention nor left any deep traces in later maps. If its influence can be traced at all, it is merely in an indirect way through Münster, who utilized materials from Wied for his *Cosmographia*. As for Herberstein, he knew of this map but did not use it because the materials at his own disposal were much more reliable; consequently, the map he himself compiled turned out to be more exact.

Sigismund Herberstein

Sigismund Herberstein, born in Styria (1486-1566), was from his early years familiar with Slavonic languages. He studied at Wien University, graduating as Bachelor of Laws. Entering the diplomatic service, in 1516, gave him the opportunity to visit many European countries including Russia. He was twice at Moskva — in 1517 and in 1526.[12] There, Herberstein's knowledge of Slavonic languages favoured his intercourse with local inhabitants, and his academic education gave him a desire for knowledge of the country so little known in Western Europe. He missed no opportunity to question people he met, not only on the customs and laws of the country, but also on its geography, particularly that of the border regions. He verified the information he collected by cross-questioning different persons on the same subject,

and he also tried to obtain various written documents and records of itineraries. He also attempted to obtain maps but these were very scarce and were kept strictly secret by the authorities. Thus he tried to persuade those whose knowledge he could trust to prepare maps for him — we have already mentioned the request made of Lyatsky. Herberstein does not mention whether he succeeded in obtaining cartographic materials from any other persons. But he certainly obtained plenty of oral information and some graphic material too. For example, we know that Grigoriy Istome and Vlasiy and Gerasimov, separately, described to him the navigation from the mouth of the Severnaya Dvina around Scandinavia to Denmark.

Finally, in the 1540's, Herberstein began sorting his collected materials and writing his notes. The first edition of his *Rerum Moscovitarum commentarii*, containing a copper-engraved map, appeared in Wien in 1549. This map, however, was preceded by another, which had been engraved under the same title by Augustin Hirsvogel three years earlier (Figures 26 and 27). Its larger format (56x36) probably explains the production of a second map of reduced size (26x16). The only notable alteration in the second map, other than the omission or addition of a few names, is the introduction of the Solovki [Solovetskiye Ostrovy̆]. Other editions appeared in 1548, 1551, 1556, 1557 and 1560.[13] In comparing these maps, one must keep in mind that the re-engraving of a map never produces a perfect copy of the original. Certain divergencies in the disposition of the names and their writing will always occur. Despite certain of these obvious differences, all of these maps are, in essential contents, quite similar. There is less information than in the Wied-Lyatsky map but they give a more exact

FIGURE 28. 1556 edition of Herberstein's map of Russia (5:3), a wood cut with forests covering most of the country. Courtesy The British Library Board.

schematic representation of Russia. An exhaustive critical analysis of the historical-geographical data provided by Herberstein, both in his text and his maps, has been made by Zamýslovski[(1884a) 514-539]. However, it is now somewhat out of date because a number of early maps have been discovered and several new historio-geographical works have appeared.

As for general ideas on Russian geography, Herberstein definitely destroyed the belief in the existence of mountain ridges in central Russia, the Ryphei and Hyperborei montes crossing Russia in a longitudinal and latitudinal direction respectively. He states that there were mountains only in the east, beyond the "Peczora" (Pechora), where lay the "Montes dicti Cingvlvs Terrae", and in the south in the Caucasus; the plain of Central Russia is characterized by lakes and rivers. He also proved that the Dnepr, Volga, Don and Zapadnaya Dvina rivers have their sources in lakes. Actually the first person to put forward this hypothesis (and to indicate the anomaly of the current conception of Russia in his day, i.e. that all the great rivers flow from mountains), was Matthew of Miechów in his description of Sarmatia; but it was Herberstein's authoritative opinion which forced acknowledgment of the lakes as the source of these rivers in Central Russia. We might have expected the incorrect representation of Russia's hydrographic map, which had been accepted earlier by Waldseemüller, to disappear; but this did not happen — to the very day of the publication of Herberstein's notes, cartographers continued to utilize for their representation of Central Russia the old materials of Waldseemüller, and not those of Matthew of Miechów.

Zell

In 1536, for example, Heinrich Zell published a map (Figures 29 and 30) of Europe in eight sheets[14] in which he utilized Waldseemüller's 1516 map and some other materials for the littoral of the Baltic and Central Muscovy; in the process he introduced a few corrections. For example, the Sea of Azov, Dnepr basin and Tauric Chersonese have acquired new shapes and new names, although the Azovskoye More is given essentially the same outline as in Ptolemy. The Dnepr (Borysthenes in its upper course and Neper in its lower) rises in a hilly and wooden place (but not from mountains!). At its sources are seen "Smolensko", "Beresina flu." and "Reytza"(Rechitsa). Here, too, debouches the "Sosa"(Sozh) with "Homla"(Gomel'). The "Prepectus" (Pripyat') joins the Sosa from the right at the town "Visegrod" (Výshgorod); just downstream the Desna joines from the left bank opposite "Kyeff"(Kiev). Upstream on the Desna are indicated

"Charnidou"(Chernigov), "Starodob"(Starodub), and "Potivla"(Putivl'). Below the Desna live "Die Rother Reussen".

The Dnepr, in its lower course, joins the Bug below the "Schwartzwald"; upstream the Bug divides twice; still further upstream is "Nougarda" (Novgorod Volýnsk?). At the sources of the Pripyat' is seen "Russia" and "Reyssyeb". Here is "Lake Amadoca" which gives rise to the Bug as well as to the affluents of the Dnestr — this is Podolia. Thus it is apparent that in addition to material from Waldseemüller, Zell utilized other materials which are new to us, possibly some from the map of Wapowski (1526).

Bernard Wapowski

Very little is known on the source materials used by Bernard Wapowski (c.1470-1535) for his map of Eastern Europe. We have referred to him previously in connection with the *tabulae modernae* of 1507 produced by Marcus Beneventanus. That Wapowski provided materials for Beneventanus' map is proved by the fact that such insignificant Polish place-names as Radochoniza and Vapowicze (Radochonice and Wapowice) are recorded: Wapowski was born at Radochonice and Wapowice was his patrimonial estate! It is known that Wapowski also produced other maps of Eastern Europe some of which served as base maps for other cartographers such as Zell, Mercator and others [Buczek(1966)36]. Perhaps this explains why A. Ortelius does not even mention his name in the catalogue of cartographers appended to his atlas published in 1570. Later, in 1579, Ortelius does include in his catalogue:

> "Florianus, Tabulam Sarmatiae, Regna Poloniae et Hungariae utriusque Valachiae; nec non Turciae, Tartariae, Moscoviae, et Lithuaniae partem comprehendentem, Cracoviae 1528".

This Florian is none other than the printer of Krakov, Florian Ungler, who was granted in 1526 a privilege to print three woodcut maps of Bernard Wapowski: a map of Sarmatia, in a northern and a southern part; a map of Polish lands; and a map of Baltic countries. The originals of these maps, which Wapowski edited during the years 1526-1528, have not survived because of a fire in 1528 which destroyed Ungler's printing shop. Our knowledge of them comes from other maps derived from them. However, in 1932, Kazimierz Piekarski found in the binding of some account books fragments of some old maps; two of them were of the southern map of Sarmatia (Figure 31)[15]. One of them forms almost all of the northeastern quarter of a map, the other almost all of the southeast-

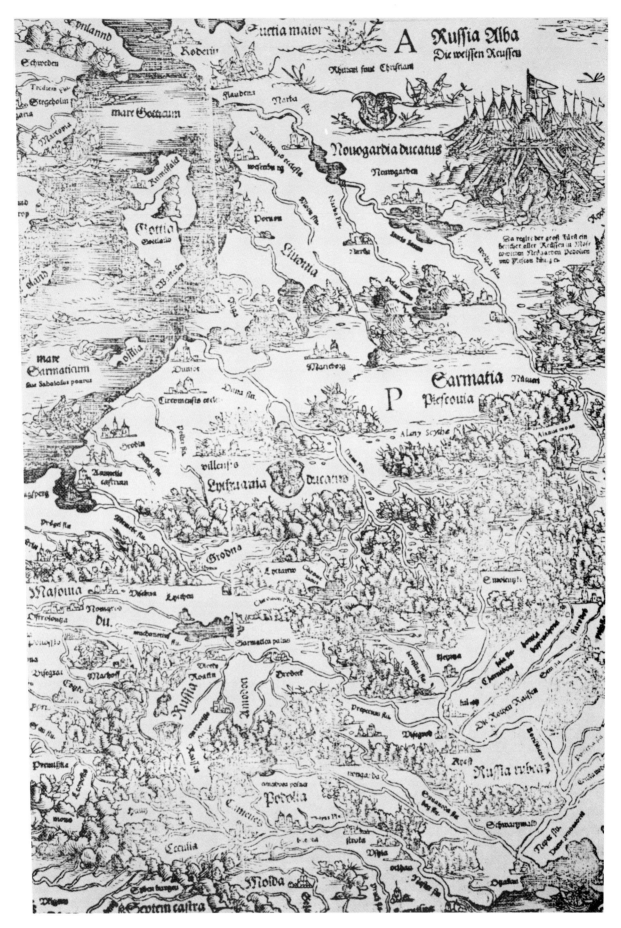

FIGURE 29.   Part of the map of Europe by Heinrich Zell, 1535, slightly reduced (9:8) from Buczek(1966)T.9.

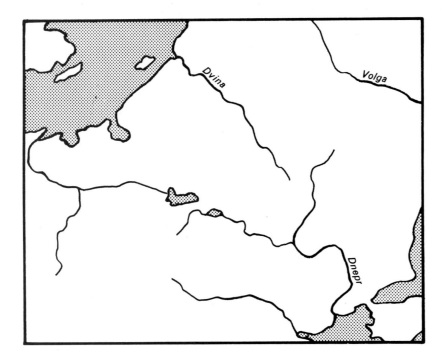

FIGURE 30.   Sketch map of Zell's 1535 map shown in Figure 29.

ern quarter — only a narrow strip of about 15 minutes of latitude is missing between them. In the north, the map is limited by the parallel of Moskva — 53°; in the south, the parallel of Constantinople — 42° 30'; in the east, the meridian of the mouth of the Don — 63°; and in the west, the 51° meridian. Apparently, the whole map comprises the same territory as was later represented by Münster in his map "POLONIA ET VNGARIA XV NOVA TABVLA" (incorporated in his 1540 edition of Ptolemy) (Figure 34) and represents a somewhat abridged and simplified copy of Wapowski's map.[16]

Wapowski's 1526 map did not, however, conform with Beneventanus' 1507 map. If this latter map was indeed made by Wapowski, we can see how much work he applied during the intervening nineteen years in order to produce a more perfect representation of European Sarmatia. We will not dwell at length here on these fragments of Wapowski's map because a detailed study of Münster's map, which we assume to be a copy of Wapowski's, is given below. Nor can we describe the Central European portion of Zell's map of Europe because in the only extant copy that sheet is missing. However, we can presume it to be very similar to Wapowski's map. Nothing is hitherto known on the northern sheet of Wapowski's map of Sarmatia as neither the map proper nor any fragments of it has yet been found.

In the same way that the works of Matthew of Miechów, Herberstein, Gerasimov, Lyatsky and Wapowski contributed new materials for cartographers of eastern Europe, the works of Jacob Ziegler

and Olaus Magnus provided new materials for cartographers of the north. While their products supplanted that of Claudius Clavus, they presented little that was new concerning Russia.

Jacob Ziegler

Jacob Ziegler (1470?-1549) was a Bavarian scholar of divinity, history, astronomy and geography. He taught at the university in Wien but travelled extensively. During his repeated visits to Roma, he met there several high dignitaries of the Scandinavian clergy including Erik Walkendorf, Archbishop of Trondheim, and Johannes Magnus, Archbishop of Uppsala, who related to him materials on Scandinavia. Ziegler's principal geographical work(1532)[17] had several maps appended to it. One map, serving as an illustration to the chapter entitled "Schondia,...", represents all of northwestern Europe — from "Gronlan" (Greenland) to, and including, the Gulf of Finland (Figure 32). It carries the following title on its verso:

"Octava Tabvla continet Chersonnesum Schondiam, Regna autem potissima, Norduegiam, Sueciam, Gothiam, Finlandiam, gentem Lapones."[18]

For the first time Scandinavia is represented here elongated from north to south and not, as on earlier maps, drawn out in its breadth. However, the eastern part of the map shows how scarce still was the material available in the West on Russia. The map is

FIGURE 31.   Fragment of a proof print of Wapowski's map of southern Sarmatia (5:4) from Buczek.

bounded in the south by the 54th parallel and in the east by the 80th meridian. On the north coast of the Finnish Gulf are the towns "Hango" and "Vibvrgh"; on the southern littoral, facing Výborg, is the mouth of an anonymous north-flowing river which empties "ALBVS LACVS". Two other rivers flow to the south from this lake: "BORISTHENES", and "TANAIS". Along the western one, the Dnepr, is found "SOMOLENZKI" and further south "ORZRA". On the eastern river, the Don, are found "MOSKAVA" and "CHLOBA". Between these two rivers, close to the lake, is the city "RESAN". Between the Dnepr and the "MARE BALTIVM" lies "SARMATIA" with the towns "NEOGRODA" and "REVALIA", and in the west "RIGA" and in the south "VILNA". The Oslo manuscript map is essentially the same although Lacvs Albvs has become a rectangular bay of the Finnish Gulf and has three rivers emptying into it; "Rivalia" lies to the west of Riga; "PLESKOVA" appears and "POLOSKO" replaces Vilna.

Olaus Magnus

The Uppsala Archbishop Johannes Magnus was also in Roma at that time. There he was preparing a description of Scandinavia; however, he did not want to encourage competition for his brother, Olaus Magnus, and thus probably did not give the above description to Ziegler. Olaus (1490-1558) began to travel in northwestern Europe and to collect information as early as 1518. In 1518-19, he visited the extreme north and in 1525 he went to Germany, Holland and Poland. Having established residence in Danzig, he then began to prepare a map of the southern coast of the Baltic Sea from Lübek to Reval. At some point, he came to Venezia where his brother Johannes helped him publish an expanded version of this map which included the Baltic countries and Scandinavia. The map (Figure 33) cut on wood in 1539, for the first time shows the Baltic Sea with three gulfs: "MARE FINONICVM Sive Sinvs Venedicvs" extending nearly SW-NE; "MARE LIVONICVM" (The Gulf of Riga) which is separated from the sea by the islands of Dagö (anonymous but for the name "Dagerort" placed below the island), "Osilia", and "Meme"; and "MARE SVETICVM".[19]

The data collected by Magnus are very extensive and new. East of Reval, along the coast, we find two castles: "Borcolv̄" and "Telsborg" — i.e., Borkholm, built as late as 1479, and Telsborg, built in 1471. Of special interest, from an earlier time, is the words "PRELIVM GLACIALE" found near the head of Mare Finonicvm on the central, ice-covered part of this gulf. Here, in remembrance of Aleksandr Nevsky's victory over the Swedes in 1240, are pictured two armies: the Russians massed at the mouth of the Neva and the Swedes galloping across the ice from Finland. There are also references to the 1241 German penetration into the Vodskaya Pyatina and to the battle on the ice of "Peybvs Lacvs" (Lake Peipus) in 1242; a mounted horseman who has cast away a bow and arrows and the note "Perdita pvgna"; and another mounted horseman crossing the frozen Lake Peipus.

Regarding the limits of Muscovy at this time, the map is, as a rule, very poor as it barely reaches Greater Novgorod. The map is full of drawings that represent features related to the climate, ethnography, zoology, people and history of the country. For example, we have mentioned several military scenes relating to various battles; in addition, there are numerous pictures of various means of transportation. The Russian Tsar is shown seated on a throne holding a sceptre with a legend "Magnvs princeps moscovitarum".

In the far northeast lies "OCEANVS SCITHICVS"; to the south, "LACVS ALBVS", with two cities, "Berga" and Starigvr" on its northeastern coast. Still further to the south, "FLV NYGEN" (the Neva) appears as a kind of channel linking the Finnish Gulf to a river which rises in two sources in mountains in the north, flows past "Kexholm" and then past "FLV NYGEN" and on to the south paralleling the edge of the map until it reaches "NOGARDIA". Here the map author notes "Non sint in vobis scismata I corī. I". Northwest of Novgorod lies "Lacvs Irmen" (Il'men'); we cannot tell if it is connected with Novgorod by a river because this space is taken up by a coat of arms and an explanatory text. The "Flv Pela" (Pola) empties into Il'men' from the south. There is a reference here to its saline sources at Staraya Rusa. Another river, the "Flv: siolana" (Shelon), flows into the southwest corner of Il'men'. The Il'men' empties into the Finnish Gulf through an anonymous river and lake. At the coast, on one bank of this waterway we find "IVANGROT" (Ivangorod) and on the other "NARVIA LIVONIE". Obviously, the author has committed an error in believing Il'men' to be the lake of Pskov since the pair of consecutive lakes represented here evidently should mean the lakes of Peipus and Pskov. Magnus has of course drawn Peipus to the west with the aforementioned mounted warrior on it. This lake also empties into the Finnish Gulf via a river reaching the gulf near Borkholm. This "Peipus" is also connected in the west with another lake through the river "Flv:vbre" (the lake is Výrts'yar' and the river is the Embach). Northwest of Il'men', the anonymous river has two unnamed rivers falling into it (apparently the Luga and the Plyusa). Next to the eastern river lies "LANDVERN". Evidently, it is the city of Gdov but for some unknown reason it is given a Swedish name resembling Landskrona — the fortress on the present site of St. Petersburg.

Thus we see that Olaus Magnus failed to obtain

Karte des Nordens nach Jakob Ziegler's Schondia. Straßburg 1532.

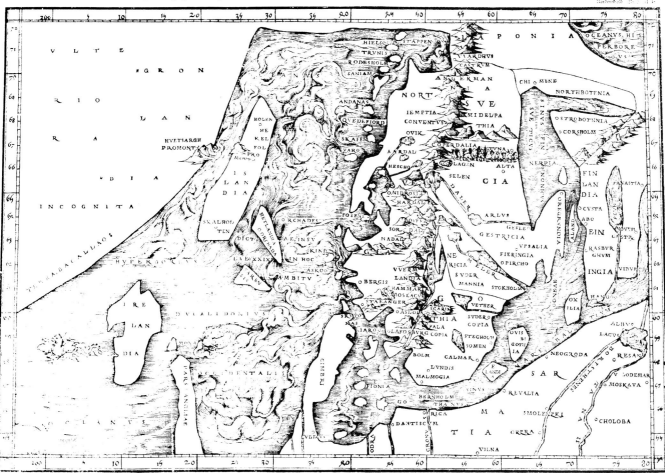

FIGURE 32.   Jacob Ziegler's map of the North, 1536, (2:1).

precise information about the easternmost part of the Finnish Gulf and its eastern littoral. Evidently his material was obtained from a small number of persons. An examination of the eastern-most parts of the Finnish regions to the north also suggest that neither Olaus Magnus nor his well-informed sources had ever travelled so far east. Despite these shortcomings in this part of the map, the map as a whole gives a great deal of information which at that time was entirely new to western Europe.[20]

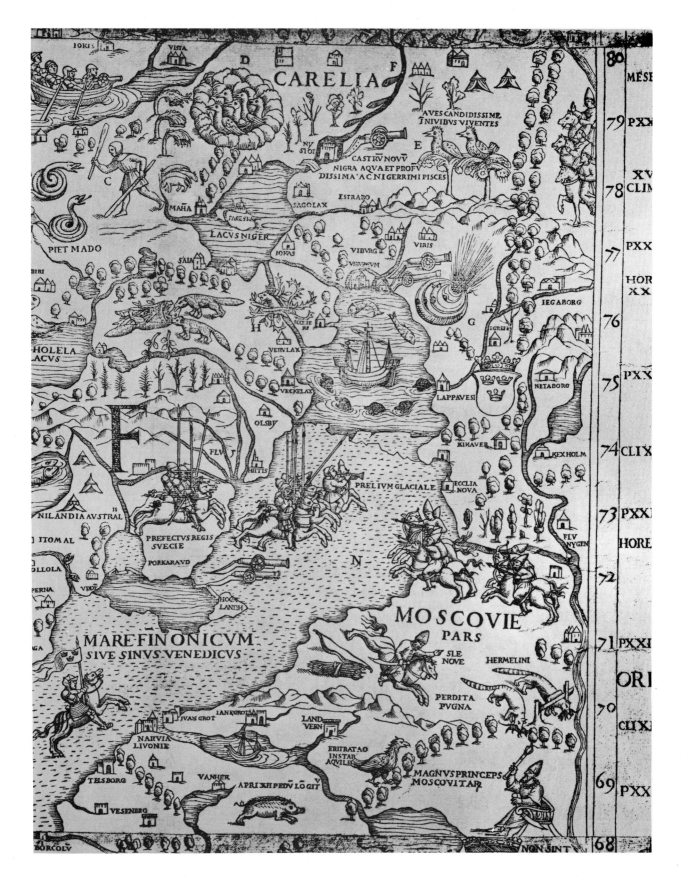

FIGURE 33. Southeast corner of Olaus Magnus' map of the North, 1539, reduced one third (3:1).

CHAPTER 7:

INCREASING PROFESSIONALISM

By the middle of the sixteenth century, a considerable amount of cartographic and geographic information had been accumulated — most had been supplied by various eye-witnesses rather than from second hand accounts. As a result, the maps prepared from them are generally of higher quality and greater complexity. Since each individual map could serve as a subject for a detailed study of its own, we shall, henceforth, consider only the unusual aspects of individual maps as well as those aspects of them which contribute to the continuity of our story. The middle of the sixteenth century also sees the greater participation in map making by scholars and other specialists rather than by travellers and other amateurs.

Sebastian Münster

Sebastian Münster (1489-1551) is one of the best-known geographers of this period. Münster was not a traveller but a scholar who collected materials from various sources and elaborated them for his own purposes. It is difficult to say when he first conceived the idea of making a cosmography but we know that more than fifteen years were spent collecting and preparing materials for it. Simultaneously, he served as a professor of Hebraism and prepared a number of other geographical works for publication. We shall consider these only insofar as they have a bearing on our subject. From this period of Münster's scholarly activities there is preserved a copy book[21] into which Münster has copied a number of maps of Ptolemy and Waldseemüller. Probably the notebook was compiled as a way of collecting materials. In addition, Münster published a guide(1528) on the use of instruments in the astronomical determination of geographical location, in which he made an appeal to scholars and travellers to send him maps and sketches. We have already dis-

cussed the possibility of an earlier appeal for information in our discussion of Matthew of Miechów who died in 1523. In any case, the geography of the whole world, which came out of this process, enjoyed a wide and fully deserved circulation during the rest of the 16th century; in all, it appeared in 27 German, 8 Latin, 3 French, 3 Italian, 5 English and 1 Czech editions.

Münster has left us several works specifically related to the cartography of Russia. These include the "TABVLA MODERNA SARMATIE..." in the Strassburg edition of 1513, which Münster had copied into the above-mentioned copybook, probably from Beneventanus' map in the Roma edition of Ptolemy, 1507; and a small map which he received from "Matvei of Mekhov" which Münster included together with his commentaries in a 1538 volume of works by Caius Julius Solinus and Pomponius Mela. We have already considered these maps (p. 51). Münster's next map (Figure 34) relating to Russia is the one included in his 1540 edition of the *Geographia* which was published in Basle. The map, "POLONIA ET VNGARIA, XV NOVA TABVLA"[22] is, of course, a copy of Wapowski's map. The eastern third of the map refers to Russian territory being bounded in the north by the sources of the "Neper fl.", "Smolensky", and "Moschia". Practically all of the Crimea is shown, together with the basin of the Dnepr. The latter matches exactly that in Zell's map of Europe mentioned above. This suggests that both Münster and, before him, Zell used the same original for their maps. The author of this original had fairly good knowledge about the middle course of the Dnepr. The absence of some important details may be charged to Münster who, on the one hand, may have considered it superfluous to fill his maps with such detail, and, on the other hand, did not know what to retain. Thus, for example, in the upper course of the Dnepr below "Orstha" there is found "Tayona noua", a hamlet with little significance; on the other hand, Stary Bykhov (upstream) and Rogachov (downstream) are

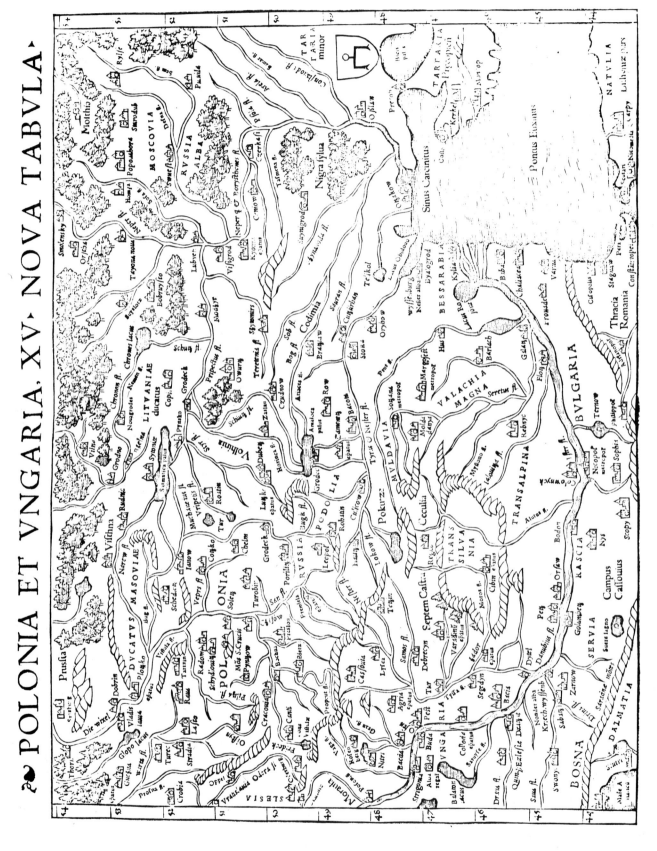

FIGURE 34. Münster's map of Poland and Hungary from his 1540 edition of the *Geographia*, (3:2).

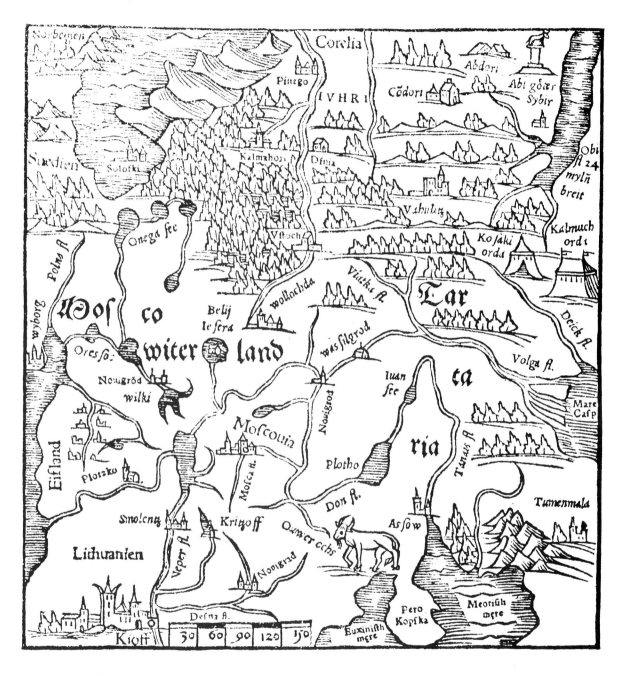

FIGURE 35.   Map of Russia from Münster's *Cosmographia*, 1544, at scale (1:1).

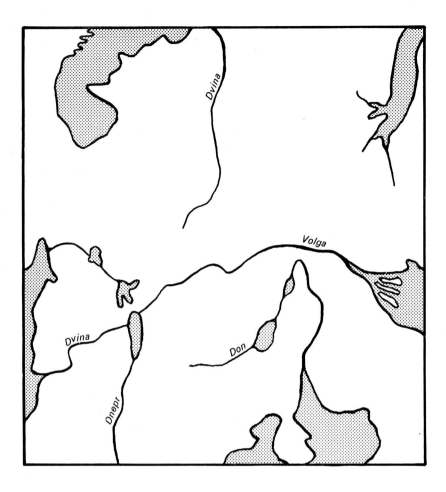

FIGURE 36.   Simplified version of Münster's 1544 map of Russia.

not mentioned despite having some history behind them.

The Pripyat' basin gives rise to several questions. One of the affluents of the Pripyat' rises in the lake "Sarmatica palus" which is also the source of the "Narew" and the "Muchaneaus" (an affluent of the Zapadnaya Bug). A southern affluent of the Pripyat', the "Horinca", rises in the "Amadoca palus" from which the affluents of the Dnestr flow south. One of the latter is evidently Smotrich since the town of "Grodec" (Grudek) has been placed beside it. Obviously the sources of all these rivers had been drawn in quite an erroneous manner. One might assume that the Pinsk marshes had been mistaken for the large "Sarmatian" lake; however, other southern affluents of the Pripyat' and other northern tributaries of the Dnestr are shown flowing from the mountain just west of Amadoca palus. Further, the "Schutz", a northern affluent of the Pripyat', flows from a lake — "Chrones lacus" — which also serves as the source of the "Nemen fl." (Neman). Since we assume that Münster used the material of Wapowski for his map, we must conclude that either Wapowski had little knowledge of eastern Poland and Belorussia, or else Münster made mistakes in copying the original map.

Later (e.g. in Mercator's map of Lithuania which also used the same original) the Sarmatian lake has been divided into two parts. Narew rises in a small western lake, while Mukhavets flows from Sarmatia lacus, the source of an affluent of the Pripyat' which joins it at Pinsk.

Of equal interest is the city of "Osslam" on the left bank of the Dnepr's lower course. Beauplan calls it Aslan; earlier Makovski places here "Ostam Kirmen, Arx murata Tartarorum". Perhaps this is in the neighborhood of Berislav where earlier there was the Tatar fortress, Kyzyakermen. To what Zell had already given one may add that Münster places "Rylse" (Rýl'sk) at the upper course of the "Sem fl.". At its confluence with the Desna is "Swuest"; most probably it is Sosnitsa, but it could also be Novgorod-Severskiy. Below Kiev on the Dnepr are "Caniow" (Kanev) and "Czerkasi". One right bank tributary is the "Tasmena fl." (Tesmin); the Ros' has been drawn but not named. On the Bug we find "Bratzlaw". West of the Dnepr liman lies "Otzakow" (Ochakov). However, beyond the small stream is a deep bay — "Lacus Obidouo" — the mouth of Dnestr. On the right-hand edge of the map is a coat-of-arms within which is a figure resembling a beam balance. Kordt has voiced

Ccrcvi   Das fünffte buch
Sarmatia Asie.

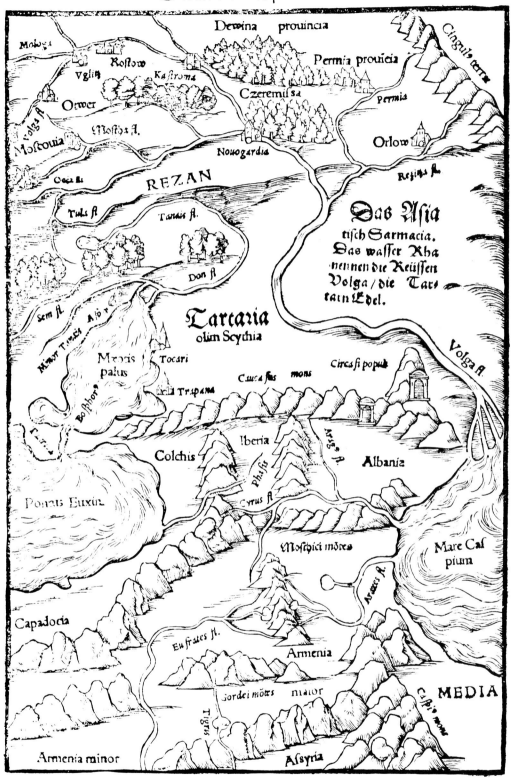

FIGURE 37.   The map of Sarmatia Asie from the 1550 edition of Münster's *Cosmographia*, slightly reduced (8:7).

FIGURE 38. Sarmatia from Honterus' *Rudimenta Cosmographica*, 1542, at scale (1:1), courtesy The John Carter Brown Library.

the opinion that this might be the trade sign of the printer or engraver. The author is of the opinion that it is one form of Yaroslav's family mark with which his silver was marked and which later was known as the Ukrainian coat-of-arms — the trident. The author came across a similar sign in the discussion of the travel of an anonymous medieval Franciscan who referred to the flags of the Tartar rulers of Norgancia or Comania and Tana. This flag is also represented on the Catalan maps of 1339 and 1375.

Even in Münster's further works one can readily see which maps he used as prototypes. In his *Cosmographia*, which first appeared in 1544, he included on a separate sheet the small map (Figures 35 and 36): "Muscowiter lands newe beschreibung". In the immediately following editions, this map was made a regular part of the text; beginning with 1550 it was somewhat enriched regarding names and, in addition, its southern part was shown to be forest-clad where previously no vegetation was shown.[23] This map is simply a reduced copy of the map of Lyatsky-Wied, which was made in 1542, but not

printed by them until 1555. Münster, however, had it in his hands before this latter date and thus was able to publish his own version as early as 1544. A contemporary bibliographer, Gessner(1548) indicates the existence of a "Lithuaniae tabula per Antoniu) Vuied" and somewhat later, (1551), he includes a picture showing an auroch hunt. The auroch, or European bison, appears at the bottom of Münster's map of 1544. Münster may have had at first only Wied's handmade map, but as early as 1548, when it became known to Gessner, it was sent to both Gessner and Münster in the form of a galley proof. On the basis of this, Münster supplemented his map of 1544 and made a fresh wood-block; the old one was probably worn out because of the large number of copies of the *Cosmographia* which were made from it. In the new edition 15 names were added and 5 omitted, the latter evidently through the engraver's oversight. Otherwise this reduced copy of Wied's map has no other supplementary data, and the only license taken by Münster is the extension of the Estonian coast down to the mouth of the Dvina. On the other hand, even

FIGURE 39.   Portion of Gastaldi's World Map of 1546 reproduced at an enlarged scale (1:3), courtesy The British Library Board.

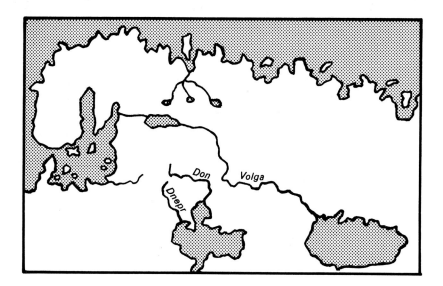

FIGURE 40. Sketch of The European part of Gastaldi's World Map of 1546.

the original received from Wied may have represented this coast in a similar manner — it is impossible to know since this place in Wied's printed map is taken up by an explanatory text and a description of Muscovy.

The 1550 edition of the *Cosmographia* also included a map of "SARMATIA ASIE" (Figure 37). While it is based on Herberstein's map of Muscovy, it does show some alterations.[24] Thus, the Don no longer has a common source with the Oka. In the south, the map is supplemented by the inclusion of Armenia. Two cities , "Tocari" and "Trapana", are shown on the eastern shore of the Sea of Azov.

Another map found in Münster's *Cosmographia* of 1550 is "Sarmatiae Landtafel". Actually it is a map of Poland and of Russia as far east as the Don. This map, however, was published earlier — not by Münster, but by J. Honterus who issued in 1542 a small cosmographical primer. It has several maps (Figure 38) attached to it including the aforementioned map.[25] Finally, we should mention that the very short text on Muscovy contained in the *Cosmographia* does not provide enough material for making the maps of Muscovy that are inserted in the book. Accordingly, these maps are supplementary to, rather than illustrative of, the text. This gives them special significance and thus their role is not neglibible.

Jacopo Gastaldi

We now pass to the work of the Venetian engineer Jacopo Gastaldi, one of the most prominent 16th-century cartographers. We know nothing about the dates of his birth and death nor about his educa-

tion. He was evidently born early in the 16th-century. His work was done in Venezia, where he was in government service as an engineer. He had the title of "Cosmografo della Republica Veneta". Archival data on him ceased in 1565 and the last maps prepared by him appeared in print in 1568 (Padovan province, the Gulf of Venice) and 1570 (Lombardy).[26] To be sure, most of his maps are based on foreign material since there is no evidence to show that he travelled in distant countries. However, a number of hand-drawn maps of the Venetian territory show that he himself made surveys for maps. His activity in making original maps extended even to other regions of the Italian peninsula.

During some 25 years of active life, Gastaldi produced a number of editions of a general world map — the first of which, a copper-engraving, appeared in 1546 (Figures 39 and 40). In 1548 its reduced copy was included in his edition of Ptolemy. Around 1550, this map was cut in wood by Mattheo Pagano. Finally, a new edition appeared in 1562. All of these editions differ somewhat from each other but the territory occupied by Russia remained unchanged.[27] Except for the reduced size copy (i.e. that of 1548), all of these maps show several rivers falling into the "Oceano Sythico". One of these is formed by three rivers rising in lakes: Vologda is found on the eastern one; "Vstiuga" lies on the central one. To the south, lies lake Biancho from which a river flows west into the Finnish Gulf; just above it "Nougardia" lies along a smaller river also emptying into the Gulf. The Volga also rises from lake Biancho and before turning south is joined by another tributary falling from the northeast from "Beloseria". Downstream a very large tributary, with the city of "Casam", joins the Volga. In the Volga Basin we also find "Mosca", "Cologna", "Rozan",

FIGURE 41. Gastaldi's map of Muscovy, 1548, at scale (1:1). Courtesy The British Library Board.

and "Citrasani" (at the mouth of the Volga). In the Don Basin — the cities of Tula and Tana. All of this is typical for maps of the early 16-century, and possibly of an even earlier period, if one considers the river system. However, among Gastaldi's more specialized maps the information on Russia changes. For example, the map of the Danubian countries, 1546[28], also includes the upper courses of the Dnepr, the Zapadnaya Bug and the Dnestr as well as all of the Prut. As the scale of this map is very large all details can be read easily. The map somewhat resembles Münster's above mentioned map "POLONIA ET VNGARIA,XV NOVA TABVLA". Thus Wapowski's influence on Gastaldi is seen here.

In 1548, Gastaldi reprinted in Italian Münster's 1540 edition of Ptolemy and supplemented it with new maps made by his own hand. The scale of these maps is small (about 12x7) and accordingly they are not rich in detail. Of these new maps, the four which refer to Russian territory in one way or another are:

1. Prvssia e Livonia Nova;
2. Schonlandia nova;
3. POLONIA ET HVNGARIA NOVA TABVLA;
4. MOSCHOVIA NOVA TABVLA.

The first map is based on that of Olaus Magnus. A few details have been left out, the drawing is simplified, and its outline has been changed to some extent; on the other hand, nothing new has been added.

The Schonlandia map was derived from Ziegler. Its southeastern corner, relating to Muscovy, is simplified even more than in Ziegler's map. The sources of "Rha seu Volga fl." are very near the Baltic Sea. "Moscovia" lies in a region bounded in the south by the sources of the Volga and in the north by the Baltic Sea. To the west, and almost touching the sea, are the sources of the Tanais. The entire course of this river is shown. At the great bend of the Don we see "Arae Cesaris". No other details are given.

The third map, that of Poland, is Wapowski's map in a somewhat simplified and reduced form. Finally, the map which interests us most is that of Muscovy (Figure 41)[29] We already noted that this map is closely related to that of Dmitriy Gerasimov in the atlases of Battista Agnese. However, it would be wrong to say that Gastaldi's map is a copy of the map of Gerasimov and Agnese. It would seem, however, that both Agnese and Gastaldi utilized an unpublished sketch by Paulus Giovio. However, both introduced numerous corrections of their own. Those made by Agnese were less discerning than Gastaldi's. To be sure, it is also possible that Agnese published Giovio's map without any amendments. If so, the errors, which hardly could have been made by Dmitriy Gerasimov, are to be attributed to Giovio. To begin with, Gastaldi gives no name to the river which lies west of the Severnaya Dvina — Agnese calls it "pecerra"? The Sukhona and Yuga remain in their apparently reversed positions relative to the Severnaya Dvina. On Agnese's map it appeared possible to go by water from the Baltic Sea past Novgorod, on a lake, to a large lake, "palus magna", from which flowed the Volga, Dnepr, and the Zapadnaya Dvina. This is not possible on Gastaldi's map as there is no Neva Basin. "Nouugardia" lies on a small lake which drains to the southeast into the "Laco biancho" from which the Dvina flows west and the Volga flows east. The Dnepr rises from a separate lake, "fonte de Neper". Gastaldi's map is generally richer in geographical names and most of the country is forest-clad. No other important differences are seen.

The four maps were also included in new editions of Ptolemy, e.g. *La Geografia di Clavdio Tolomeo*, published by Girolamo Ruscelli of Venezia in 1561 (as "MOSCHOVIA NVOVA TAVOLA"), and in subsequent editions in the years 1561, 1564 and 1574. These maps were on a somewhat larger scale (24x18) and included a few errors in names, apparently caused by a new engraver.

Likewise, with some additions, Gastaldi published in Venezia in 1550 the map of Muscovy (Figures 42 and 43) which was appended to the first Italian edition of Herberstein's notes.[30] Gastaldi gave the map a graduated frame and a trapezoidal projection. He based his additions to this map on Herberstein's text as well as on the information he had received from abroad. The Neva Basin has been developed further; Lake Ladoga is represented and has a connection with the Volga by way of Il'men' and the "Sna" River. The portion of the Baltic coast from the Neman to the Narva follows Olaus Magnus. The Dnepr Basin has been entirely revised and comes close to Wapowski's data. The aptly drawn forest and hills make this copper-engraving a kind of perspective map. In the corners, outside the map-frame, are shown various animals. Gastaldi's map can therefore not be considered as a simple copy of Herberstein's map for in some parts it is considerably revised in the light of new information. In addition, it also fully satisfied contemporary scientific requirements as regards its projection and the graticule. Perhaps the best proof that it met contemporary demands is the fact that it enjoyed wide circulation as a separate map. It was also included in a number of atlases of Antonio Lafreri as a separate sheet and was also repeatedly reprinted by other publishers — in many cases the animals presented outside the frame in the upper corners (areas left free because of the map's trapezoidal projection) were replaced by various drawings accompanying Herberstein's text, primarily the Muscovite Tsar on the throne, speciments of coats-of-arms and even a mounted warrior.

The last work of Gastaldi related to Russia was a large two-sheet map which he published in 1562 (Figure 44). It evidently also met with success, as in 1568 fresh blocks were needed, or else the right to print the

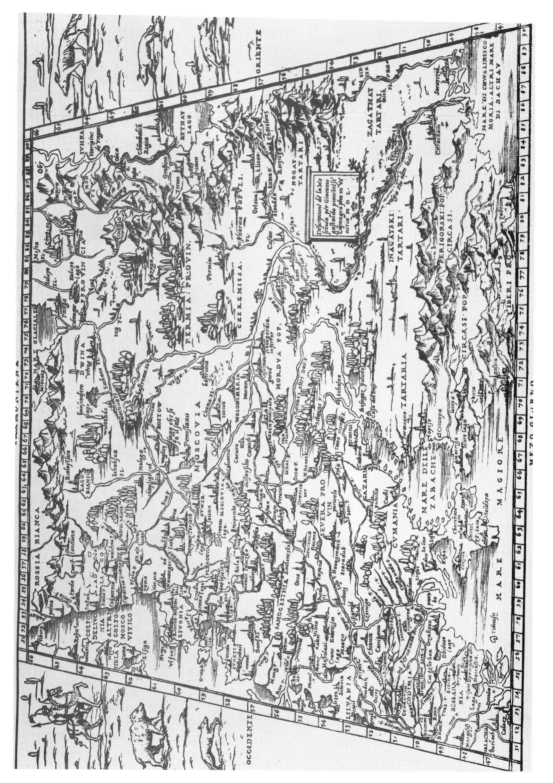

FIGURE 42. Map of Muscovy published in 1550 by Gastaldi appended to Herberstein's notes. Scale (9:5). Courtesy The British Library Board.

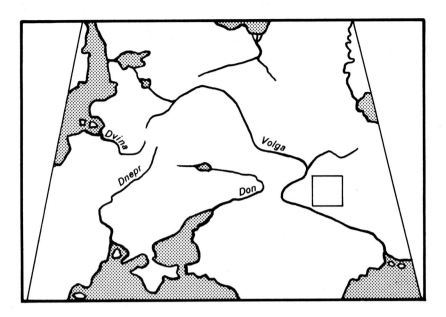

FIGURE 43.   Sketch of Gastaldi's 1550 map of Muscovy.

map was given to an additional publisher. The two editions are essentially identical.[31] The only variation comes from the elimination of a few names in the outer frames of the 2nd edition, necessitated by the reduction in width of the 2nd edition: the northern sheet to 50.5 cm and the southern sheet to 48.8 cm from a uniform 52 cm in the 1st edition. The scale remained unchanged. The map is bounded in the north by the Arctic Ocean,in the south by the Danube, in the west by the Vistula Basin and in the east by the Sura river and the Kerch' Strait.

By 1562, when Gastaldi first published this map, the cartographic material on which he could draw had become quite rich. In 1554, Mercator's large map of Europe had been printed. In fact, it was the main source for Gastaldi, although he changed somewhat the design of the rivers, lakes, etc. In addition, Gastaldi omitted a number of geographical names or altered them because he failed to read them correctly or to understand what they represented. For example, where Mercator has "Soloffky cenobium", Gastaldi has left out the first word and transformed the second into "Sonobio"; "Iuagrot" has become "Louagrod" (Ivangorod); and "Wotzka regio" became "Vozca Reg" (Vodskaya Pyatina, i.e. the Vod region of Novgorod). The system of small lakes to the west of the Severnaya Dvina is given an outlet to the east via "Waga Lago" into the Dvina; here Mercator places a description of Muscovy in a frame. The "Pinega flu" joins the Dvina near its mouth. Gastaldi, however, shows two Pinega rivers: one joins the Dvina from the right near its mouth; the other is shown as a separate river to the east falling into "MARE SITHICO". Immediately to the east, Gastaldi shows a stream of similar size with the town "Yuri" in its middle sec-

tion; in Mercator, the town is "Juhri".

Especially annoying are some of the spelling errors made by Gastaldi. For example, the letter "L" has been substituted for the first letter "J" to produce such names as "Laroslavie" ("Jaroslaw" in Mercator) and "Lorgouiz" ("Jorgowitz"). "Nisni Nowgorod" has been turned into "Nisui", while the second half of the name — "Nouigorod" has been placed to the north on the opposite bank of the Volga. Instead of "Susdal", there is "SVDAL PRINC".

There is the possibility that Lafreri used Gastaldi's name as bait for customers at a time when Gastaldi was not in a position to make and edit all the maps that bore his name. During 35 years of active life Gastaldi turned out more than 40 works among which there were monumental endeavours such as the world map (1546-1562), new maps for Ptolemy's *Geographia* (1538), a map of the Danubian countries on four sheets (1548), two maps drawn on the walls of the Palace of the Doges in Venezia (1549 and 1553), maps of Asia on six sheets (1559-61), southeastern Europe on four sheets (1559-60), Italy on three sheets (1561), Africa on eight sheets (1564), and others. It is clear, therefore, that Gastaldi was hardly able to check and supervise every detail of all these maps. Moreover, we know he also was charged with conducting and supervising various maintenance and improvement projects relating to the lagoon and canals of Venezia. In saying this, we do not wish in any way to detract from the value of Gastaldi's contribution. His fame as one of the greatest cartographers of the 16th-century, at the side of Waldseemüller and Mercator, is safely established, even if he had given little in the way of new original material concerning Russia.

FIGURE 44. The northern sheet of Gastaldi's 1562 map of Scandinavia, Poland and Russia. Scale here approximately (3:1). Courtesy The British Library Board.

Gerardus Mercator

Now we turn to the third of the trio of famous 16th century cartographers — Gerardus Mercator (1512-1594). Younger than the two preceding ones, he was born in East Flanders where he spent the first half of his active life. His first printed cartographic work — a globe (around 1534-37) — was made in collaboration with Gemma Frisius under whom he studied at the Louvain University. Mercator's cartographic work continued from this time. In 1552, he moved to Duis-

FIGURE 45. Northern Russia as shown in the top two sheets on the right of Mercator's Map of Europe, 1554. Scale (7:3). Courtesy The British Library Board.

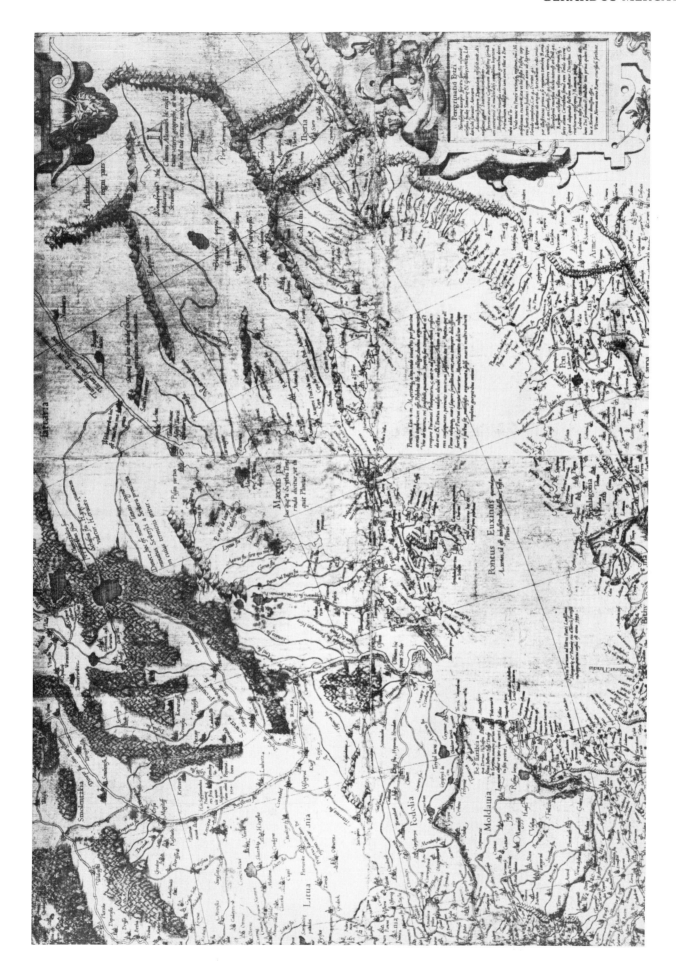

FIGURE 46.   Central Russia as shown in the middle two sheets (below those above) in Mercator's 1554 map. Courtesy The British Library. Board.

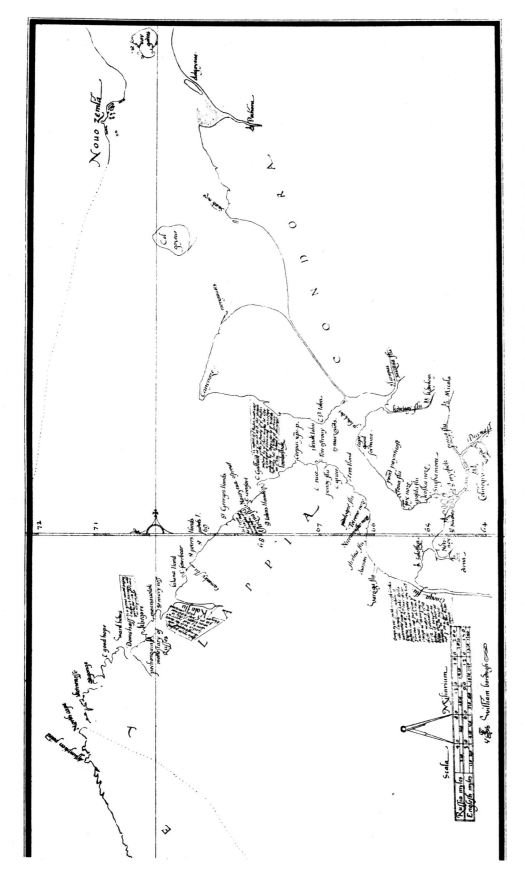

FIGURE 47. William Burrough's map of the northern coast of Scandinavia (3:1). Courtesy The British Library Board.

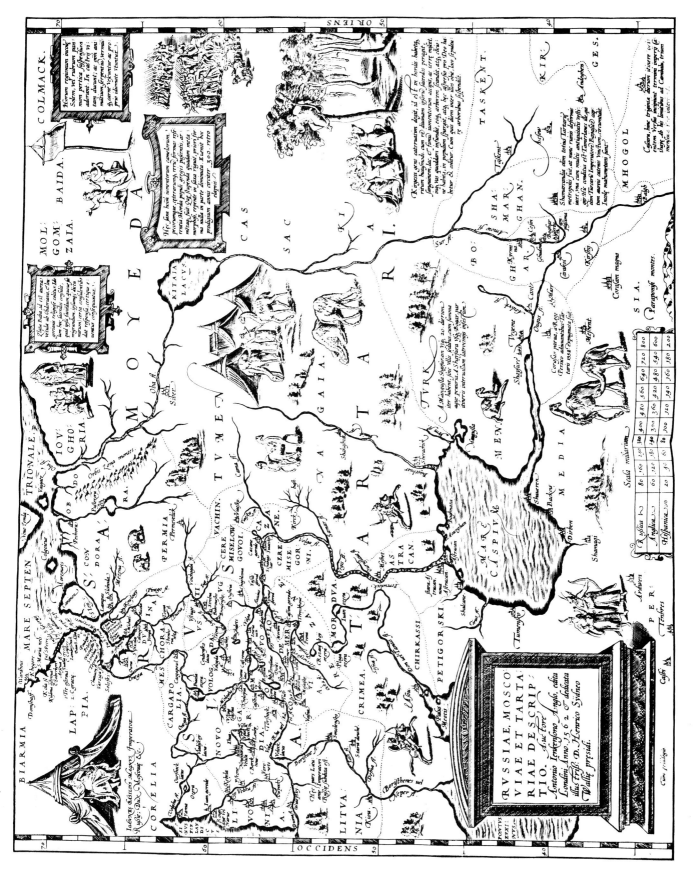

FIGURE 48.   Ortelius' 1570 edition of Anthony Jenkinson's Map of Russia, at half scale (2:1).

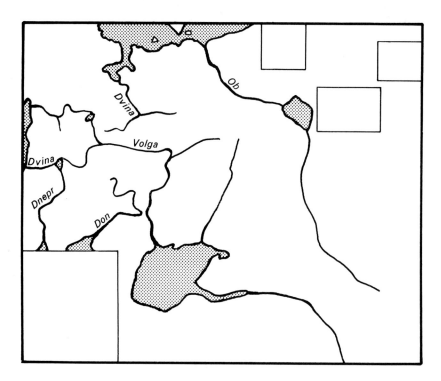

FIGURE 49.   Sketch map of Jenkinson's Map by Ortelius.

burg in Germany. It may be said that map-making in general and the production of copper-engraved maps only then began in Germany. As early as 1554, Mercator published in Duisburg his large map of Europe (Figures 45 and 46).[32] Mercator used different materials for his maps with somewhat greater discernment and caution than did Gastaldi. We cannot ascertain as yet all of the sources of his material on Russia other than those things which had already been published. However, new materials in his maps are in no way marked by richness and generally refer to routes of communication from the West to Muscovy. For the northern and part of the central regions of Russia Mercator used Wied's maps. The Baltic countries were taken from Olaus Magnus, or perhaps even from Wapowski if the latter's map had reached Duisburg. However, even these materials have some corrections indicating Mercator's possession of some other sources of material on Russia. For example, the province of Koborge (Koporye) from Wied's map has been moved to the coast as an inhabited place "Coperoia". A new "Wotzka regio" (Vodskaya Pyatina) has appeared. Perhaps, Wapowski may already have known this? Wapowski is the source of all of western Russia, the basins of the Dnepr, the Zapadnaya Bug and the Dnestr. Because of the conic projection, the Volga, below where it approaches the Don, falls outside the map frame. It is clear, however, that Mercator had no new data on this part of Russia, but rather used that from Catalan maps. The region between the Volga and the Don is "Pereuoloca"

(Perecolok or Portage); here we see "Tuia". The well-known city of Tula, spelled "Tulla" by Mercator, is in its approximately correct position. Downstream from the above-mentioned portage, the Don is entirely unknown to Mercator so that he follows Ptolemy for the rivers, cities and the coast of the Sea of Azov. Upstream on the Don lies a small unnamed river with the city of "Vich", and then another tributary, the "Mez" (Kracivaya Mech?) and the town of "Lechi" (Yelets). Finally, near its source, we find "Donko" (Dankov).

One should regard Mercator's world map of 1569 as the next step forward. His fame dates from this map, for here he first used his famous projection in which the distance between parallels increases toward the pole. However, in order to understand this and subsequent cartographical works by Mercator and his heirs, we should stop to consider some of the new materials on Russia which began to appear in the second half of the 16th-century. We should recall that the rivalry of Spain and Portugal in the discovery and exploitation of new lands in the East and West Indies made it increasingly necessary to define precisely routes leading to and from these lands. This rivalry also resulted in Pope Alexander IV issuing a bull in 1494 dividing the globe into an eastern (Portugese) hemisphere and a western (Spanish) one. While other countries were thus officially barred from access to these overseas lands, it did not stop enterprising mariners from making voyages and discovering new routes which could outflank the Spanish-Portugese monopoly.

FIGURE 50.   De Jode's 1578 edition of Jenkinson's map of Russia. Reduced (7:5).

English Seamen

One of these mariners was Sebastian Cabot. Born some time between 1470 and 1475, he participated in a voyage to Brazil as early as 1497. Later he became a well-known cartographer[33] in the service of the Spanish court. As early as 1516 the question arose of sending an expedition to the coasts of North America in order to find the Northwest Passage to the Pacific Ocean. However, this expedition never materialized. In 1547, he was invited to England to organize an expedition to India by a northern sea route, rounding either America or Asia. For this purpose the Company of Merchant Adventurers was founded and in 1553 the first British expedition under Sir Hugh Willoughby started out to the East by way of the Arctic Ocean. Cabot made a special instruction for Willoughby, possibly even a map. Willoughby did not succeed in penetrating the northern Ice Sea and he perished there; his companion Chancellor, however, reached the Russian coast and established relations with Moskva. In 1555, a Muscovy Company was founded in London, and its management was entrusted to Cabot. By 1565, Stephen Burrough had discovered Vaygach Island and surveyed both inlets to the Kara Sea. Thereafter, the exploration of northern Russia waters steadily advanced.

A member of the expedition of 1556 was the leader's brother, William Burrough, who apparently, prepared a map (Figure 47) of the northern coast from Trondheim to Vaygach.[34] It carries no names other than those of coastal points. In 1578, William Burrough presented the Queen with an "exact and notable mappe of Russia" which he had prepared. This map is lost, only the explanatory note with which he presented the map to the Queen is preserved.[35] Subsequently, he issued a whole series of supplemental instructions for navigation for northern Russian waters.

However, there is no doubt that the richest material was furnished by Anthony Jenkinson, another member of Burrough's expedition. He arrived in Archangel'sk in August 1557, and in Moskva on December 1 of that year, and remained in Moskva until April 23, 1558. During this time he obtained the Tsar's permission to go to Bukhara. He left Moskva by water, following the course of the Moskva river, the Oka and the Volga to Tyub Karagan on the northern coast of the Caspian Sea. There he took a caravan to Bukhara where he arrived on December 23rd. In March, 1559, he began his return journey, arriving in Moskva on September 2nd. On February 17, 1560, he proceeded northward, and reached Kholmogory on May 9th. Thus Jenkinson is the first foreign traveller known to have traversed Russia from north to south.

Jenkinson took regular notes during his travel and even undertook several latitude determinations. A table of geographical points is enclosed in his report. Whether he is the author of this table, or whether Hakluyt received it from someone else remains an open question. At any rate, Jenkinson did not personally visit Greater Novgorod, and, accordingly could not have determined its latitude. The following places were included in the table (Table IV):

Moskva	55° 10'
Greater Novgorod	58° 26'
Nizhny Novgorod	56° 33'
Kholmogory	64° 10'
Vologda	59° 11'
Kazan'	55° 33'
Uvek	51° 40'
Astrakhan'	47° 9'
At the entrance to the Caspian Sea	46° 27'
Mangýshlak on the sea-coast	45° 00'
Urgench in Tartary, 20 days travel from the Caspian Sea	42° 18'
Bukhara, city in Tartary, 20 days travel from Urgench	39° 10'

TABLE IV

Immediately upon his return to England, Jenkinson seems to have started preparation of his map of Russia. Its original has not come down to us but the map is known by its two printed editions. One was included in Ortelius' 1570 edition of the *Theatrum orbis terrarum* (Figure 48 and 49) and the other in Gerard de Jode's atlas, *Speculum orbis terrarum*, 1578 (Figure 50)[36] These two maps are fully identical in appearance and contents in those portions relating to Russia; they differ primarily in their scope. The De-Jode map represents only the north-western part of the map included in Ortelius. In other words, the eastern half of Ortelius' map (lying east of a central meridian passing near the mouth of the Ob' and the Yaik) and the lower third of the western half of the map all represent additions to the De Jode version. The important question as to which of the two is Jenkinson's original map remains open. There are several possibilities: that the map actually had the scope given by Ortelius's map; or that the eastern half was added — possibly by the engraver — in order 1) to make its format conform to the atlas, and 2) to save the cost of preparing a separate map of Central Asia, a

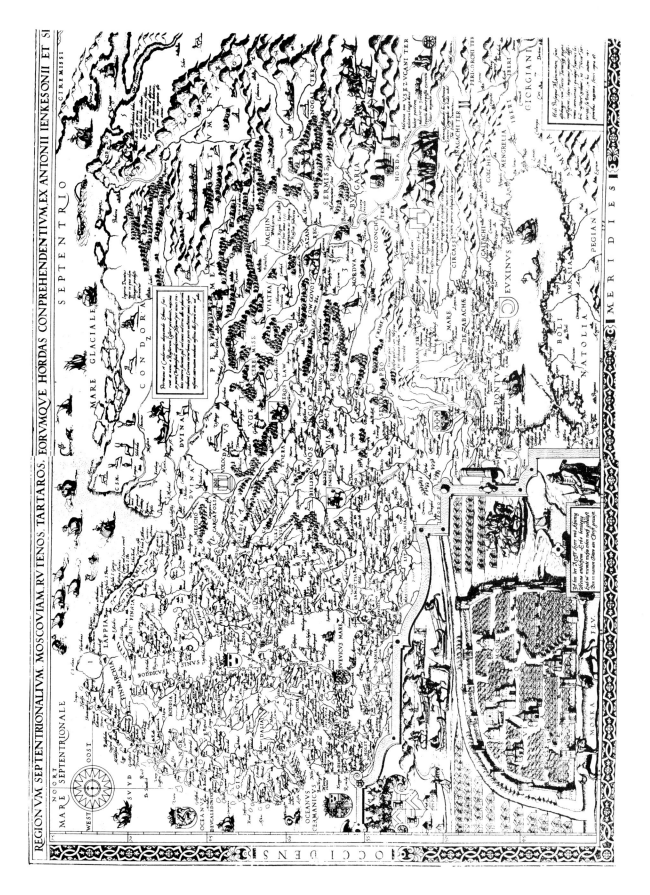

FIGURE 51. The left two sheets of Deutecum's three sheet map of the period 1562-1569. Scale (3:1).

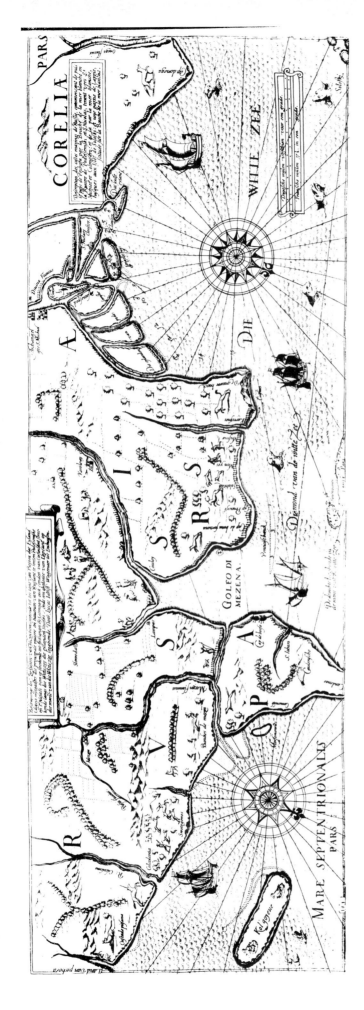

FIGURE 52. Russia's northern coast from Onega to Pechora from Waghenaer's *Thresor der Zeevaret*, 1592. Reduced (7:3).

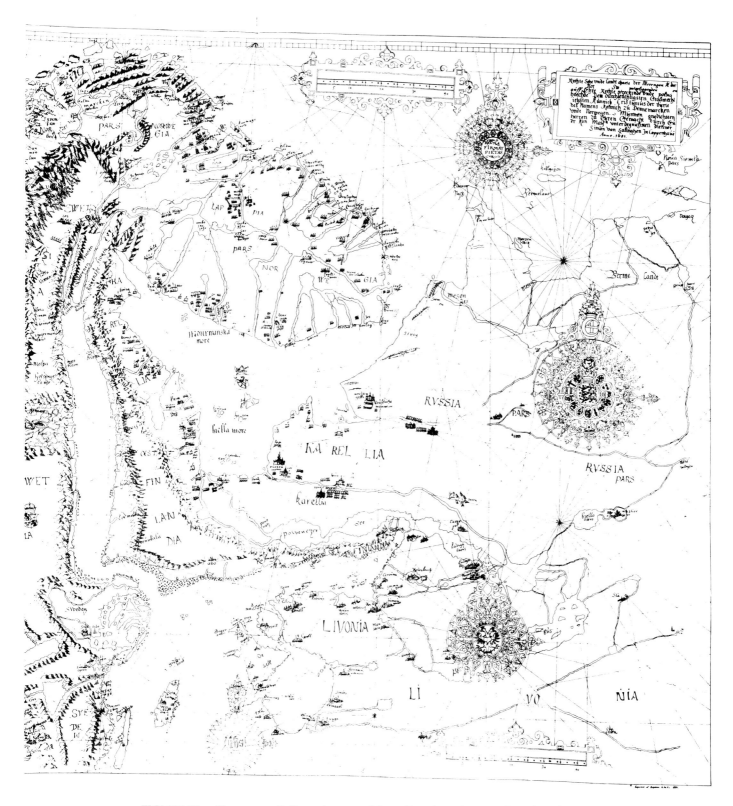

FIGURE 53. Simon van Salingen's map of Scandinavia, 1601, greatly reduced (5:1).

venture for which adequate material was probably lacking.

We do not propose to solve this problem but are inclined to assume that Jenkinson's original is closer to De Jode's map. This belief springs from the fact that Ortelius's map is adorned with various figured designs that are typical of Netherland map-engravers and do not resemble English products. On the other hand, one would think that Jenkinson's original map was prepared in England.

Despite the fact that Jenkinson was the first Westerner to traverse Russia from north to south, his map is a step backwards, not forward. Apart from its northern coast and the routes from Archangel'sk to Moskva and down the Volga to Mangyshlak, the rest of the map is a relapse into an earlier representation. The sources of the map are apparent: for the north — Burrough's map; for the east and south — Wied; the middle and lower course of the Volga reflects Jenkinson's own impression, although the extreme southeast beyond the mouth of the Volga (found only in Ortelius' version) is probably the work of an engraver or cartographer who enlarged Jenkinson's map at Ortelius' request. Here, the Caspian Sea is shown in its entirety with its western coast clumsily bent around to the east. This is probably not attributable to Jenkinson, for his original map was printed during the three year absence from England (beginning May 15, 1561) during which Jenkinson went to Persia by way of Moskva. There is indirect evidence indicating that Jenkinson's original map did not show the Caspian Sea, for in his world map of 1569, Mercator accepts Ptolemy's and not Jenkinson's unorthodox outline of the Caspian Sea. But in a discussion with Humphrey Gilbert (after 1576) Jenkinson asserts that in his general map of Europe of 1572, Mercator had utilized all discoveries made by the English in Muscovy and in the northeast. For his world map of 1569, Mercator would certainly have used the newest delineation of the Caspian Sea if it had been known to him. Thus, Ortelius, or possibly even his engraver, may have been encouraged to enlarge Jenkinson's original map, and to add at least a few names on the Caspian west coast utilizing the account of Jenkinson's most recent travels to Persia. In Ortelius' map there is a figure of Ivan IV seated on the throne of Russia. The figure is in the northwest corner of the map — the same place as the map-title in de Jode. Could it be that it was placed there to fill the void created by moving the title to the bottom of the enlarged map?

There is another map which is connected with Jenkinson's name. A three-sheet map (Figure 51) printed in the Netherlands, engraved by Johannes and Lucas à Deutecum, [Doetecum][37] with the title: "REGIONVM, SEPTENTRIONALIVM, MOSCOVIAM..." The map title then goes on to state that it was compiled on the basis of the itineraries (descriptions of travels) of Jenkinson and Herberstein but not on the basis of Jenkinson's map. It is therefore possible that an original Jenkinson map does not exist at all. The map also contains a large number of figures which evidently refer to a text which was published separately and probably was to be attached to the lower part of the map. As a rule, the place names, unfortunately with all their errors, have been taken from Jenkinson. But despite the map's title, the main source of information seems to have been Mercator's map of 1554. However, the eastern and northern parts of the map do not tally at all with the manner in which Mercator later represented them in his 1569 map. Therefore it must be assumed that the three-sheet map was made some time before 1569 but after 1562, the year when Jenkinson's map was supposedly published. This would explain why Ortelius' version of Jenkinson seems to have borrowed all of its eastern part from this three-sheet map and not vice versa. This is an additional reason to assume that the map printed by Ortelius was not an original map prepared by Jenkinson but a map whose eastern part was supplemented so that it should fit the format and design of Ortelius' atlas. A comparison of the Ortelius and the de Jode versions seems to indicate that the three-sheet map stands closer to De Jode than to Ortelius.

A map of greater interest is that appended to an account made by Jenkinson's Italian rival, Raphael Barberini.[38] It is difficult to say whether Barberini made it himself or someone else made it for him. It would seem that it was prepared for his travels particularly for his 1564 trip to Moskva. Since not all names have Italian forms — some of the original ones are written in German — it would seem that the map was drawn by an unknown German and that Barberini wrote Italian names in his own hand over some of the German place names. Details in the map mostly refer to the Baltic area north of the Duna — from the sea to Narva, lake Peipus and the Velikaya river. Beyond this, only the largest cities and principal geographical data are given. These geographical details, few and schematic as they are, are quite precise. The sources of the Duna, Volga and Dnepr are shown close to each other but as separate sources (not from a common lake). Likewise, the Volkhov empties into *ozero* Ladoga, from which flows the Neva. This sketch-map, an enclosure in a private trade report, remained unknown to contemporary cartographers and was therefore never used by them.

In addition to Jenkinson, Chancellor and Burrough, there were many other Englishmen who travelled in Russia collecting various data. Richard Johnson, Jenkinson's travel-companion, gathered information about routes from Russia to China, Permia, and Persia. Arthur Edwards (1567) gathered in Astrakhan' material on Persia and on different routes

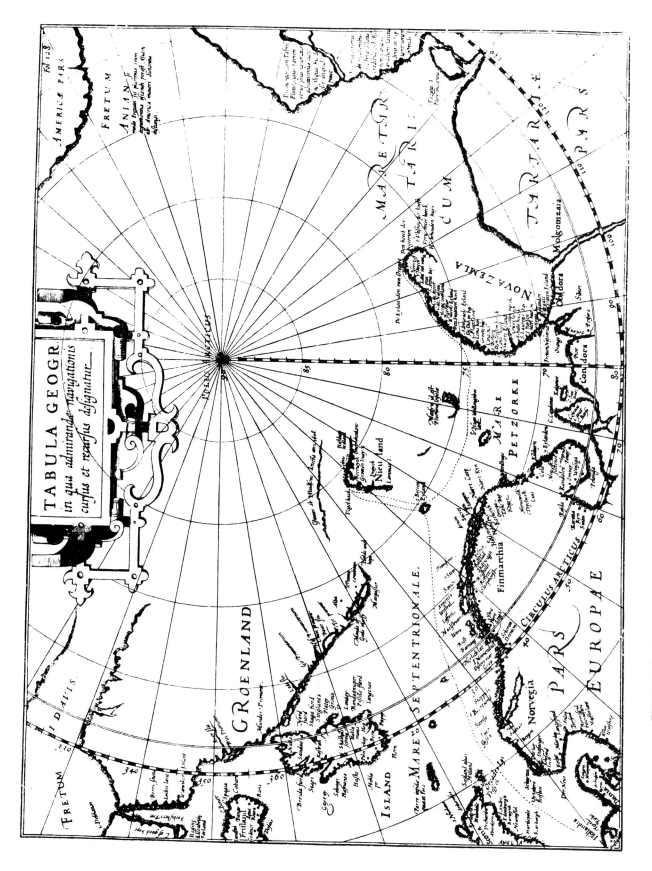

FIGURE 54. Barents' map from his third Arctic expedition as published by Hondius, 1611. Scale (3:2).

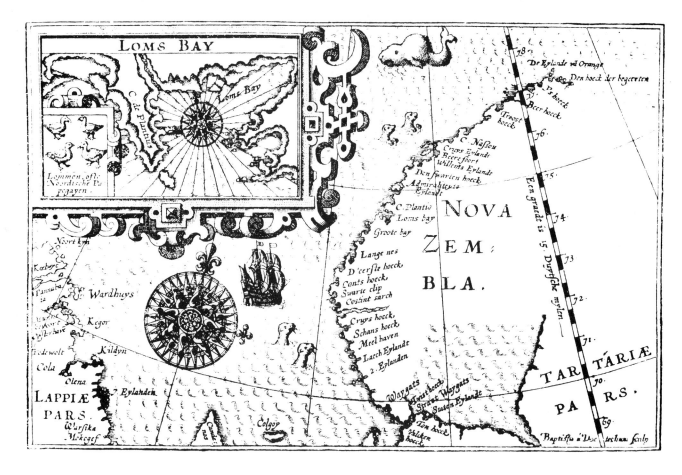

FIGURE 55. Map of the Barents Sea from the North Cape to Novaya Zemlya by de Veer, 1598, reduced slightly (6:5).

within Russia. William Burrough's nephew, Christopher Burrough, travelled to Persia and determined longitudes and latitudes of points on his way from Archangel'sk to Astrakhan', and sent this information to his uncle (1581). These and other similar materials have been collected and published by Hakluyt.

Polish Cartographers

During the intervals between the Mercator maps of 1554, 1569 and 1572, a number of maps of countries adjacent to Russia were published by other catographers. Some of these also contributed knowledge on Russia. The western regions of Russia, for example, were frequently shown on Polish maps. We have already mentioned (p. 72) the first Polish cartographer to bring the knowledge of the Polish lands to the West — Bernard Wapowski. He was followed by a succession of Polish cartographers which included Waclaw Grodecki (Wenceslaus Grodecius) - 1558; Andrzej Pograbka (Andreas Pograbius Pilsnensis) - 1570; Maciej Strubicz (Matthias Strubicz) - 1589: and many

others.[39] Likewise, we have already mentioned a number of maps of Scandinavian and Baltic countries, such as that of Olaus Magnus; others include C. Antonisz (c.1543), M. Tramezini (1558) and L. Algoet (1562).[40]

Dutch Mariners

The north of Russia was known not only to the British, but also to the Dutch. Lucas Jansz Waghenaer (his Latinized family name was Aurigarius) was a well-known Dutch navigator who published a number of sea atlases. His second sea atlas *Thresor der Zeevaret*, 1592, — included a sea map (Figure 52) of Russia's northern coast from Onega to Pechora.[41] The first Dutch ship came to the mouth of the Severnaya Dvina in 1577 or 1578, and the Dutch soon became rivals of the British in trading with Muscovy. In the text to the above-mentioned map, Waghenaer notes that Olivier Brunel is the discoverer of "that country" (Novaya Zemlya) and the one who tried to reach China by the northern sea route.

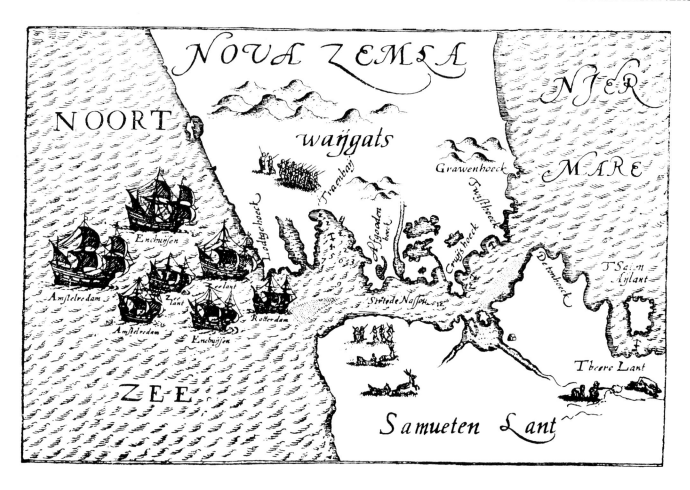

FIGURE 56.   de Veer's map of the Yugorskiy Shar, 1598, (6:5).

Brunel came to Kola on one of the first Dutch ships. From Kola he went to Kholmogory to study Russian. Because of some offence he was imprisoned; from prison he was taken into the service of the Stroganov family of merchants. At the Stroganov's order, he travelled into Siberia as far as the mouth of the Ob', and descended the Pechora to the sea. In 1581, he took their merchandise to Antwerp and to Paris to sell and went to Holland to invite skilled seamen to serve on two sea-going boats built by the Stroganovs. On these ships, Brunel tried to go to China by sailing around Siberia. But after this attempt failed in 1584, he returned home to Enkhuizen where Waghenaer lived. It is this voyage that Waghenaer mentions in his text. Accordingly, the map of the northern coasts included in his *Thresoor der Zeevaert* is undoubtedly Brunel's work.

In 1566-7, Simon van Salinghen and DeMeyer, two Dutchmen, went secretly from Kola to Moskva by way of Onega and Kandalaksha. Having visited Novgorod as well, they returned home with a stock of precious merchandise and valuable observations. Salinghen continued to visit Russia during the next

thirty years. In 1584, he came to Kola as the diplomatic representative of the Danish King Fredrik II for whom he had promised to make a sea map. From 1584 to 1601, he travelled to the coasts of the Arctic Ocean four times. The resulting map (Figure 53) is dated 1601 but was obviously drawn at an earlier date.[42] Salinghen states in his account that he made, in 1570, a voyage along the coasts of Karelia and Lapland from the mouth of the Onega to Kola; during this trip he measured the depth of the ports and river estuaries, noted the distances between them, and determined the latitude and longitude of various points.

Another map was made in Holland on the basis of Salinghen's material; it was very similar to Salinghen's map although somewhat altered. It is possible that it is the map mentioned by Adrian Veen(1597)[43] as being published (or prepared) in 1589. In any case, the author of this later map, "C.D." (Cornelis Doetsz), describes it as being "very improved". Salinghen's map is characterized by a considerable enlargment of the portions of the White Sea which compresses Finland into a very thin isthmus. Salinghen knew well the White Sea coast, the interior

FIGURE 57. A third map by de Veer of the Barents Sea coast and Novaya Zemlya, 1598, (5:4). Courtesy The British Library Board.

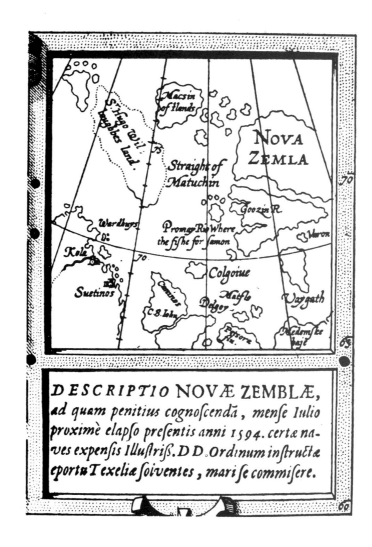

FIGURE 58.   Doetecum's map of the Arctic archipelago, 1594,
at scale (1:1). Courtesy The British Library Board.

of the Kola Peninsula, the Finnish Gulf and the Gulf of Riga. The White Sea, however, lies too far to the west and therefore distorts the positions of the Ladoga and Onega lakes (the latter is known to Salinghen as the "Povenets Sea"). The map revised by Doetsz is also characterized by an enlarged White Sea, although not to such an extreme. Doetsz' map is exclusively a sea map and is therefore limited to listing points along the coast and the river mouths. Of interest in both maps are "Russ. Narua" and "Russe Haken" — the latter lying between Narva and Koporye.

Later, in 1594, another expedition — that of Barents — started out for the north. It was repeated in 1595 and 1596. Barents was both an experienced navigator and a cartographer. Even before he set out on his first voyage, he prepared (1595) a sea atlas for navigation in the Mediterranean. As its date indicates, this atlas appeared only after Barents' return from his first or second voyage to Novaya Zemlya, in 1595 or 1596. Meanwhile, he also made new maps of

the northern coasts of Europe, which were included in the 1596 edition of *Thresoor der Zeevaert*.[44]

Barents' third expedition began auspiciously with the discovery of Spitsbergen and Bear Island but ended with his tragic death. He was compelled to winter on the north-eastern coast of Novaya Zemlya. When summer came, he resumed his travel in a sloop. However, weakened by the long winter, he died suddenly from exhaustion on June 20, 1597 while en route. It would seem that during his wintering on the coast of Novaya Zemlya he prepared, in addition to a report of his expedition, a map which was published only after his death.[45] This map (Figure 54) shows the northern coast of Europe and Asia with only a single gap between the Ob' Bay and the hypothetical island of "Tasata". The Asian coast beyond this island tallies fully with the concepts prevailing at that time which were reflected in Ortelius' map of Tartary in his *Theatrum Orbis Terrarum*, 1570, and subsequent editions. The western part has been drawn in a highly satisfactory manner considering the time. Novaya Zemlya already has the delineation of an island although only its western coast is shown. The Yugorskiy Shar ["Straet Waygats" and "Fretum Nassovicum"] is shown as a strait while the Kara Strait appears merely as a break in the western coast. The "Pitsora" [Pechora] appears as a river of quite modest size. Just to the east, the Khaypudyrskaya Guba is shown with the town "Sebiera" at its head. Beyond the Vaygach lies the Ob' estuary; the Ob' drains from a large lake — "Somer Zee' with the city of "Coscam" on its east coast. The map indicates the route of Barents' last expedition, proceeding by way of "T'veere Eylandt" (Bear Island) and "Het nieuwe land" (Spitsbergen) to the northeast coast of Novaya Zemlya. The whole space extending to the Pole is filled with whales and seals but is free of any land; thus Barents did not share the views of Mercator who filled the Arctic basin with four sectors representing four continents.

Barents' travelling companion, Gerrit de Veer, added a few maps and plans (Figures 55, 56 and 57) to his own account of the voyages.[46] To be sure, in one way or another, his works are connected with Barents' name. In respect to his map "Caerte van Nova Zembla", de Veer states in his account that it was made on the basis of direct observations by Barents and that death struck Barents at the very moment he was making notes for the map. That Barents himself had only vague ideas about Novaya Zemlya and adjacent areas (from his first expedition) is suggested by a rather primitive map (Figure 58) of the whole Arctic archipelago which B. à Doetecum published in 1594 as an inset to a much larger map of Europe.[47] It would seem that the material for the small inset map was supplied by Barents. Judging by some of the fantastic shapes found there it is obvious that the material was of dubious quality.

Caspar Vopel

Finally, let us say a few words about the map of Europe made by Caspar Vopel (1511-1561). Born in Medebach, Westphalia, Vopel spent all his life as a teacher in Köln. His first cartographical endeavors were devoted, as were Mercator's, to making globes. Nevertheless, as early as 1545 he made a large 12-sheet world map which was cut on wood. In 1555, he made a large map of Europe which is now lost. We can, however, obtain a likely picture of its contents from a subsequent edition, that of 1566.[48]

The 1566 map (Figures 59 and 60) represents an attempt to combine all the most recent information about European and Asiatic Sarmatia with the classical picture of Herodotus, Strabo and Ptolemy. Accordingly, the shape of "MAEOTIS PALVS" has been

rigidly preserved from Ptolemy and the mouth of the Don is located on the 52nd parallel, in nearly the same latitude as "Czarnithauw" (Chernigov). In the north, the map reaches the north-east corner of the Finnish Gulf whose ice-cover is reminiscent of Olaus Magnus; the Neva, Lake Ladoga, Novgorod and the Volkhov have been taken from Wied's map. Vopel follows Wied's outline fairly closely but revises it somewhat.

South of the Neva estuary, we see the influence of two different sources, as Vopel, not knowing which of the two he should trust, used them both. "Rogodif" (Narva) and Iuangrot" (Ivangorod) are located on either side of the mouth of a large river; upstream are "Niescholt", "Kobela" "Perskoff", "Ostrof" and "Opotzki". Near its mouth, this large river is joined by another stream rising to the south in lake "PEIBAS" (Peipus) which has a fairly correct location in relation to points lying west of it. Weid's influence is also seen in Central Russia — in the Volga basin. The Volga rises, as do the Duna and the Dnepr, in a common large lake — "LACVS CANDIDVS". The rivers "Viathca" (Vyatka) and "Kamma" in the northeast are drawn correctly; upstream a river "Sorna", with a city of "Onschea", empties from the north into the Volga. Here is "Nesiotis regio". In Wied's map we see the same confusion of Unzha and Chukhloma. The Don basin has likewise been copied from Wied but already the course of the Dnepr has been affected, it would seem, by Wapowski's map. Here one sees many features common to the small map "Polonia et Vngaria" which Münster appended to his edition of Ptolemy of 1540. Here, also, the "Poleni" (Polyany) live along the right bank of the Dnepr below the Pripyat'. It is interesting to see that at the side of contemporary names we find scattered adapted names of peoples given by Ptolemy.

Mercator

Let us now return to examine some further works of Mercator that relate to Russia. These are:

1. the world map of 1569.[49]
2. the map of Europe of 1572.
3. maps included in *Atlas Sive Cosmographicae Meditationes de Fabrica Mvndi et Fabricati Figvra. Gerardo Mercatore Rupelmondano.* The first edition, completed by him, appeared after his death in 1595. In this atlas were included maps relating to: a) Russia proper, b) Livonia, c) Lithuania, d) Southern Russia, e) Poland and f) Arctic regions.

A comparison of the three maps, i.e., Europe 1554, the World Map of 1569, and Europe of 1572[50] shows that Mercator was continually revising his maps. It is clear that the scale of the 1569 map (Figure

FIGURE 59. Northeast corner of Caspar Vopel's 1566 map of Europe, reduced (3:2).

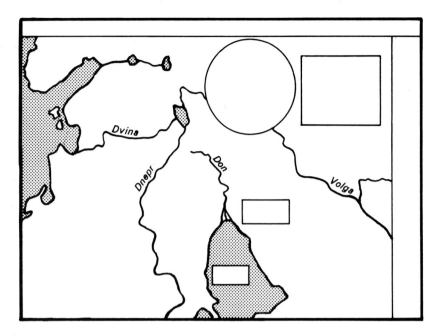

FIGURE 60.   All of the Russian lands, in simplified form, from Vopel's
1566 map.

61) is smaller than that of the two others, while the maps of Europe have preserved not only the same scale and projection but also, as regards Russia, the same printing blocks. At first glance it would seem that the scope of the 1572 map has been extended northward, but in fact only the land mass has been shifted southward allowing a fuller representation of the White Sea coast. A number of locational changes have taken place, particularly in the 1569 map, as evidenced in Table V.

	Degrees of Latitude		
	1554	1569	1572
Northern tip of Scandinavia	75°	73°	72°
Kanin Nos(Cape Kanin)	off the map	70°	70°
Solovki	74°	67°	67°
Kholmogory	70°	65°	65°
Neva	65°	64°	63°
Oesel	60°	60°	60°
Moskva	58°	56°	56°
Azov	52°	50°	50°

TABLE V

The Black Sea as well as the southern Caucasus have remained in the same place in the map of 1572 (Figures 62 and 63) for this block remains unchanged. The Sea of Azov and the regions north of the Caucasus, on the other hand, have been revised. This is not reflected in the Don basin, despite the fact that it

was engraved anew in each of the three maps. The Volga basin, and thus Central Russia, have been changed in a number of details. It is characteristic that the error committed in connection with the Kama and the Vyaz'ma has remained uncorrected on all three maps. Left-bank affluents were added in the 1569 map in keeping with Jenkinson's information, but were removed on the 1572 map.

Mercator's work, insofar as it referred to Russia, was crowned by a special map — the first one to be designated as a map of Russia — "RVSSIA cum confinijs" (Figures 64 and 65). It was included in his atlas which appeared after his death.[51] All of the aforementioned maps of parts of Russia are reflected in this general map. Thus we shall not discuss the details of the individual maps which were prepared on the basis of the maps of, chiefly, Pograbka and Strubicz and therefore repeat some of their errors, such as the legendary Polish lakes of Amadoca, Salmatia, Crona and Tur, though without giving their names. In his map of 1572, Mercator could not utilize all the materials that were now at his disposal. Thus, this latest map of Russia differs considerably in content from his map of 1572.

In the extreme north of the "RVSSIA cum confinijs" map, Novaya Zemlya has not been revised although this would have been possible in the light of the material now availble from Barents' first voyage or his third expedition. Mercator could also have taken information on northern Russia and part of Siberia from another source: on March 20, 1581, one Joann Balagh in Arensburg gave to the "Belgian" Olivier (Alferius) a letter of recommendation to Mercator.

FIGURE 61. Portion of Mercator's World Map of 1569 at reduced scale (8:5). Courtesy The British Library Board.

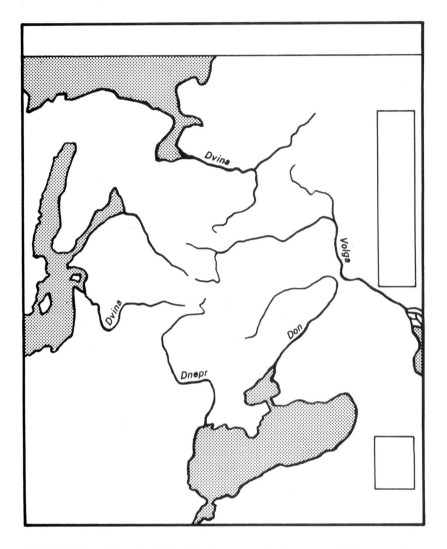

FIGURE 62.   Sketch of the Russian part of Mercator's 1572 map of Europe.

This "Belgian" is Olivier Brunel whom we have mentioned previously (p.104). Having been in Holland to hire skilled seamen, and having a letter to Mercator, Brunel could easily have given Mercator geographical data collected during his stay in Russia.

The Mezenskaya Guba (Mezen' Bay) is shown in its correct location facing the inlet to the White Sea. The 1572 map also showed a deep bay at this point with two rivers flowing into it: one unnamed and the other the "Kowloay" (Kuloy): the Mezen' bay is found to the east in the location of the Cheshskaya Guba. In the western part of this Sea, we see the beginnings of the Kandalakshskaya Guba: to the south the Onezhskaya *guba* is still missing. "Albus Lac." on the Kola peninsula is somewhat smaller and might now be taken for Lake Imandra. To the southwest, the Finnish Gulf is more closely aligned with the 60th parallel: although after the mouth of the Neva, the Gulf bends sharply north forming the Výborg bay. Compared with the 1572 map, the mouth of the Neva has moved south by 2.5 degrees. The Baltic regions

have acquired an entirely new appearance in accordance with Strubicz' map. The lower course of the Dnepr and the Dnepr basin remain practically unchanged. On the other hand, the upper Dnepr basin has been altered in light of the information given by Strubicz and Pograbka. The lower Don and its basin, the lower Volga and the Kama basin have remained unchanged except for a few new rivers, details, and names. The error in drawing the Kama and the Vyatka has been preserved.

In the lower right-hand corner of this map is appended a small-sized map (Figure 66) of central Russia — "RUSSIAE PARS Amplificata" — which serves to demonstrate the source region of all the important Russian rivers. In this respect it corresponds to the small map of Matthew of Miechów which Münster published in 1538. Without dwelling on the details of this small map, let us simply state that its reduced copies were included in a number of editions of Hondius' *Atlas Minor* until it was replaced by Isaac Massa's map. Mercator's map was also reprinted

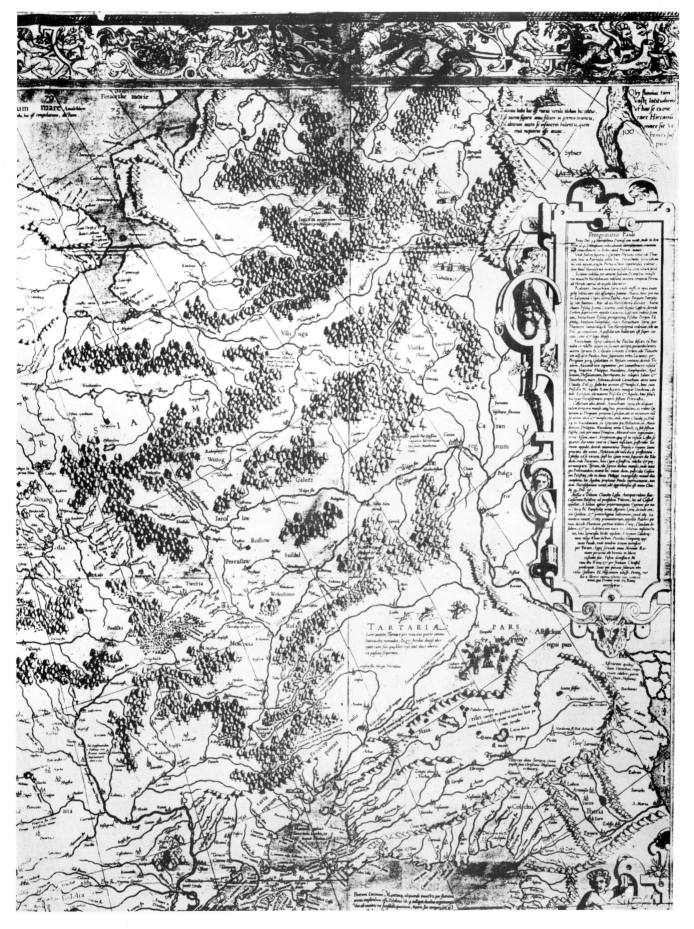

FIGURE 63. Portion of the 1572 map of Europe by Mercator.

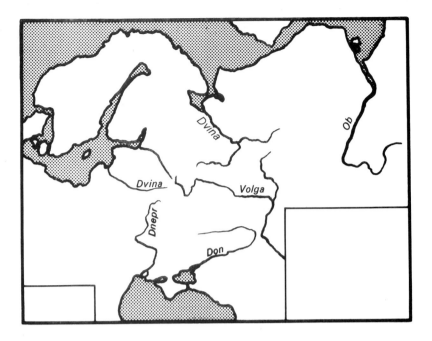

FIGURE 64.   Sketch of Mercator's map of Russia, 1595.

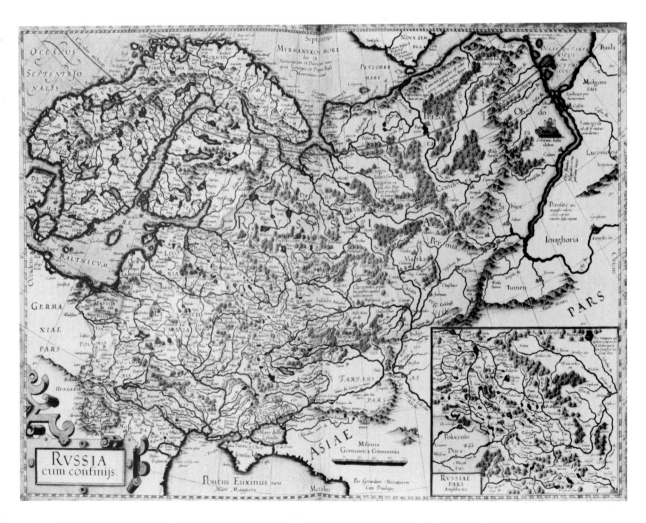

FIGURE 65.   Mercator's map of Russia from his atlas of 1595, at one-third size (3:1). Courtesy The British Library Board.

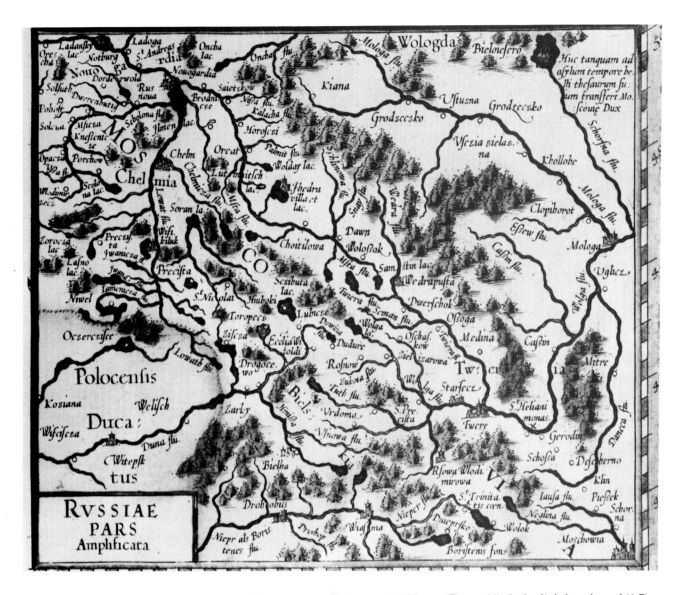

FIGURE 66. Central Russia as shown in the inset map of Mercator's 1595 map (Figure 64). Scale slightly enlarged (6:7). Courtesy The British Library Board.

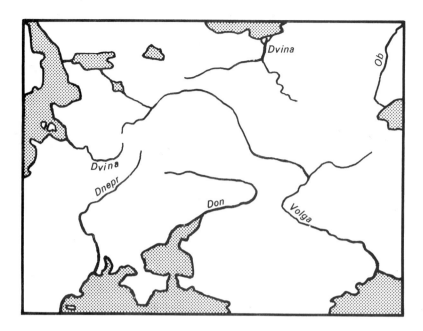

FIGURE 67. Sketch of Maginus' map of Muscovy.

by Neugebauer(1612) in his description of Muscovy.[52] Even Tsarevich Fyodor Godunov based his work on this particular map. From Godunov's map, Hessel Gerritsz and Isaac Massa in turn published their maps in Holland.

We should mention one further map (Figure 68) which was included in the Latin edition of Ptolemy's *Geographia*, printed in 1596 by Johannes Maginus.[53] It is remarkable in its large-size representation of "Ladoga Lago". "Mare Glaciale" replaces the White Sea so that the northern coast of Russia is almost entirely absent. The Kama is shown correctly. The "Golfo de Livonia Altri Golfo Moscovitico" is shown in a north-south orientation, but then we are seeing only the most eastern part which includes the Výborg bay. The rivers are drawn in a somewhat stereotyped manner, but their sources are separated. Because of its small size, it lacks sufficient detail to trace fully the influence of earlier maps. However, this map apparently was drawn as an independent work.

These maps mark the end of the 16th century and of a clearly defined period of mapping — a period when maps of Russian lands were made principally by foreigners, even if the latter at times used material supplied by Russians who then resided abroad and who may not have had exact data with them (e.g. Gerasimov and Lyatsky). At that time Russia had not yet developed cartographic work of its own and the rare maps that were made were state secrets, embracing, moreover, only small special territories. The 17th century is the century of Russian cartography and original Russian cartographical knowledge begins to find its way to the West and to influence European cartography. Accordingly, the turn of the century also begins a new and epic era in the cartographical field in Russia.

FIGURE 68. Johannes Maginus' map of Muscovy from the 1596 Latin edition of the *Geographia*. Slightly enlarged (3.4). Courtesy The British Library Board. Board.

CHAPTER 6: THE BEGINNING OF A DIALOGUE

1. "Tolmach" (interpreter) alias "Mitya Maliy" (Demetrius Junior) alias Demetrius Erasmius.

2. A Russian translation was first published by Semenoff in *Bibl. Inostrannӱkh Pisateley o Rossii*(1836) I, Part I; fragments were later printed by him in *Sӱn Otechestva*(1852)part 28(150). The complete Latin text is reproduced by Michow(1882-1883) 169-187. Finally, it was published in Russian in its entirety by Malein(1908)251-275.

3. On Battista Agnese, see Wagner (1931) who enumerates and describes in detail all the MS atlases of Agnese and other cartographers of that school known to him. A few additions to this list are given by Bagrow(1932)190, Wagner(1947)28-30, and Almagià. The map in question is, however, not included in all the atlases. It is to be found only in the following editions, according to the numbers given by Wagner:44,45,47,48,49,55,56,57,58,59,60,68, and in the one indicated "Berlin".

4. The map(32x23) was first reproduced photographically by Ongania(1881)Pl.XVII(1:1); then by Yefimov(1948)38(9:8); and Bagrow(1962)40(1:1). Michow(1882-1883)T.III(1:1) includes a traced copy; his copy is reproduced by Kordt(1899)T.III(1:1). Michow(1906)8-9 again describes the map.

5. We will shortly note what efforts Herberstein made to obtain a map of Russia and that he nevertheless failed. Later, at the end of the 17th century, when Spapharius departed on a mission to China, he took along a map of Russia and presented it to the Bogdakhan, But this caused him to be prosecuted and to fall into disgrace.

6. This was the case with d'Avril, who when travelling via Warszawa in 1686, received through Sobessky (the travel guide) a map apparently made by Venyukov, a member of Spapharius' embassy to China. As this map was published by d'Ablancourt, we can see to what extent it has been changed (we presume, intentionally) by Venyukov, who probably did not want to deny Sobessky a favour; nor, on the other hand, did he wish to betray his government. We presume the changes were intentional as Venyukov could scarcely have confused so many of the details of his journey in recording them.

7. Baddeley[(1919)I,CXVI] tries to explain this error ascribing it to a misunderstanding of the draughtsman, supposing him to have drawn them as if reflected in a mirror. This would have placed the Sukhona in its proper   orientation with Vologda to the west. Such a mistake would be natural to an engraver, but scarcely to a designer.

   Recognizing Gerasimov's unquestioned education, knowledge of ecclesiastical and historical literature, and, last but not least, his geographical knowledge, it should be noted that his familiarity with Russia was acquired from repeated journeys in the west and north of Russia. His knowledge of the southern, eastern, and even parts of central Russia, if he knew these parts at all, was only from the descriptions of other travellers; this we deduce from the fact that his autobiographical recollections, communicated to Giovio, do not mention that he had ever visited them. Also, official Russian maps would scarcely have been available to him as they did not come into the scope of the work of the *Posol'skaya izba*.

8. Kordt has reproduced both this map (1899)T.IV(1:1) and a similar one (1899)T.V(24x18) from Ruscelli's edition of Ptolemy, Venezia, 1561. The 1548 map is also reproduced by Bagrow(1962)42(1:1).

9. On this occasion, Lyatsky mentions that Herberstein had once asked him, among several other persons in Moskva, to compile a map of Muscovy.

   Wied's name is here spelled as the German transcription of the Russian which would be transliterated "Vӱd".

10. The first to discover Wied's map was Michow(1882-1883), but he described and reproduced an engraving of 1570 made by Fr. Hogenberg. An impression of the original engraving was later discovered by W. Ruge at the Ehemalige Universitätsbibliothek, Helmstedt; he put it at Michow's disposal for publication as a separate full-sized reproduction (85x82) — see Michow(1906)K.IV(3:1) and Bagrow(1962)Pl.6(3:1). Later Kordt[(1931)30-31] discusses this map and reproduces it [(T.39,40 and 41)]. Since 1913, the original has been in the Herzog August Bibliothek, Wolfenbüttel.

11. The first to reproduce Hogenberg's copy(48x35) was Michow(1882-1883)T.II(1:1). Others include Kordt(1899)T.VI(1:1) from his own copy of Nordenskiöld(1897)T.XXXV(5:4); and Bagrow(1962)45(7:5). Other articles on Wied, besides these and others mentioned above, include Michow(1905); Bagrow[(1930)104-106; and Nehring(1897c).

12. Literature on Herberstein is extensive. In Russian — the excellent monograph by Zamӱslovski(1884) and two earlier articles (1875) and (1876); and Alekseyev(1932)98-122. Herberstein's notes have been translated into Russian by Anonimov(1866) (but with no maps) and by Malein(1908). Other literature is indicated in Sobko(1886)396-397. Also see Adelung(1818).

13. The most characteristic editions of Herberstein's maps are the following:
   1) 1546—"Muscovia Sigismvndi Liberi Baronis in Herberstein Neiperg et Gvtenhag MDXLVI". A copper-engraving (56x36) by Hirsvogel, as indicated in a legend to the right: "Hanc Tabvlam Absolvit Avgvstinvs Hirsfogel Vie: Avs: Cvm Gracia Et Privilegio Impe: 1546:. This map exists only in two copies — the Österreichische Nationalbibliothek, Wien, and the British Museum, London. It has been reproduced by Kordt(1899)T.XI(1:1), and Bagrow(1962)46(3:2).

2) 1548— The same text as in the 1546 map, but with the misprints "Gvtnhag" and "MDXLIX". The legend at the right now reads "Hanc Tabvlam absolvit Avg. Hirsfogel Vie: Avs: Cvm Gra: et Privi. Imp." A copper-engraving (26x16), it has been reproduced by Nordenskiöld(1889)121(1:1); Bagrow also mentions Rovinsky(1882)T.8.

3) 1549— "Moscovia Sigismvndi Liberi Baronis in Herberstein, Neiperg, et Gvtenhag Anno MDXLIX". A wood-cut (34x21). The legend to the right has been replaced by a graphic scale giving "Distantia per Miliaria". It has been reproduced by Adelung(1818) (4:3); Malein(1908)T.2(6:5); Kordt(1899)T.12(6:5); and Belov(1956)217(2:1).

4) 1551— "Erste landtaffel: in welches des gantz Moscuiter land mit sampt den anstossenden völckeren, nach rechter geographischer art beschrieben". A woodcut, it was reprinted several times from the same block. It has been reproduced by Zamyslovski(1875)T.7 In the German editions published at Basle in 1563 and 1567, the Latin inscription is replaced by a German one.

5) 1556— "Moscovia Sigisvndi Liberi Baronis in Herberstein, Designatae syluae non carent suis incolis", a woodcut (37x26) of the Latin edition with woods. It has been reproduced by Kordt(1899)T.XIV(1:1); Malein(1908)T.1(5.4); and Zamyslovski(1884)T.VIII(9:8), but in this latter reproduction the woods have been erased. There is also a German edition of this map entitled: "Andere Landtaffel: In welcher der Moscouiten gebuet, mit sampt den walden vnd bergen auch etlichen gebreuchen, vund allen vmligenden Landschaften begriffen."
There is also a small copy(21x14) of this map appended to the Basle edition of 1556 entitled: "Brevis Exactaqve Moscoviae Descriptio". Michow[(1906)16] erroneously regards this copy as an appendix to Darinel(1555) who reproduces it (1:1). On Darinel, (or G. Boileau de Bouillon), see Bagrow(1928)45-47. This map has been reproduced by Rovinsky(1882)T.IX(1:1); Kordt(1899)(1:1); and Malein(1908)137(5:3).

6) 1557— "Moscouia Sigismunds Freyherens zu Herberstain Neyperg vnd Guetenhag ec. Berteutsch. Anno 1557". A separate legend states "Gedruckt zu wienn in Osterreich durch Michael Zimmerman in S. Annen Hof". It is a woodcut (39x27). It has been reproduced by Kordt(1899)T.XIII(1:1). An enumeration of extant copies is given by Kordt(1899)6-9. See also Bagrow(1928)106-110.

14. This map, a woodcut, was found in Firenze by the author who acquired it and described it in his(1926); see also Bagrow(1930)110-114. At present this map is preserved in the Deutsche Staatbibliothek, East Berlin. Unfortunately one sheet of the eight is missing — the first sheet, Central Europe — so that it is impossible to cite the title of the map. This extant copy is a proof impression and so poorly executed that the names are not always readable, particularly on the coast of the Sea of Azov, Taurica, and parts of the Dnepr basin. A fragment of the map, including only Poland and Western Russia, has been reproduced by Buczek(1966)T.9 slightly reduced.

Heinrich's brother, Anselmus Zell, published an explanatory text to this map in Latin (Antwerp, 1535) and in German (Nüremberg, 1536).

15. Buczek, Olszewicz and Piekarski prepared the fragments and a text for publication as part of Volume I of *Monumenta Poloniae Cartographica* [Buczek(1966)18]. The Second World War, however, prevented their publication and caused the fragments to be taken to a library at L'vov where they perished in the last stages of the war. Fortunately, some proof sheets survived; two fragments comprising the eastern part of the southern map of Sarmatia are reproduced by Buczek(1966)T.8(1:1). Buczek notes (correspondence with the editor, May-September, 1969) that the scale of the reproduction is only approximately the same as the original fragments. Assuming they are, then the total size of the combined northern and southern sheets of the map of Sarmatia would be (47x62), not (60x90) as stated in Buczek(1963)32.

Leszczycki and Modelska-Strzelecka[(1967)16] give its title as follows:"TABULA COSMOGRAPHIE PARTICULARIS NONNULLA loca regni . . . Polonie et etiam Hungarie, ac Valachie, Turcie, Tartarie et Masovie continens, Cracoviae, 1526". He concludes that it formed the basis for the maps of S. Münster (Poland and Hungary-1540), H. Zell (1535), G. Mercator (1554,1572), K. Vopel (1555-1593) 6 editions, and J. Gastaldi (1542).

Leszczycki also gives the title of the lost northern map — "TABULA COSMOGRAPHIE PARTICULARIS docatus Prussie, Pomeranie, Sanogithie et magni Ducatus . . . . Lithuanie continens, Cracocia, 1526" — and states that a map of the Balkan countries, sent by Wapowski together with the map of Sarmacia to Eckin, Augsburg in 1530, was probably used in maps of H. Zell (1535), G. Mercator (1554), K. Vopel (1555) and O. Magnus (1539).

Important literature on Wapowski includes Birkenmajer (1901) and Buczek(1966)32-40. Other works are mentioned by Leszczycki and Modelska-Strzelecka(1967)16-17.

16. This presumption was advanced by Hantsch(1898) and was later repeated by Kordt(1910)12. Olszewiecz[(1930)156] believes the anonymous map in the de Jode's atlases of 1578 and 1595 to be a copy of Wapowski's 1526 map of Sarmatia.

17. In February, 1902, the Universitetsbiblioteket, Oslo acquired a manuscript entitled "(Schondia) Ett geografiskt arbete öfver Skandianaveien från år 1532." Nissen(1956), who believes that this manuscript should be dated 1530, discusses the relationship between this manuscript and the published book of 1532.

In regard to Ziegler and his work, see Günther(1896) and (1897); Kordt(1906)5-6; Bagrow(1930)116-118; and, of course, Nissen(1956) who mentions among others the important works of Schottenloher and Storm and a forth coming edition of the Schondia by the Norwegian Scientific Academy.

18. A woodcut (35x23), it has repeatedly been reprinted by later geographers in one form or another. The map as it appeared in Ziegler's book(1532) or (1536) has been reproduced by Bagrow(1964)167(7:3); Hildebrand(1878)(1:1); Nordenskiöld(1889)57(8:5); and (1882)Pl.2(9:8). The map from the Oslo manuscript (28x18) has been reproduced by

Nissen(1956)50(2:1) and (1941)(4:3). In modified form the map appeared in Münster's *Geographia*, Basle 1540, as "SCHON-LANDIA XIII NOVA TABVLA"(34x25); Gastaldi's Ptolemy, Venezia, 1548(17x13) entitled "SCHONLADIA NOVA" from whence it has been reproduced by Lucas(1898)T.VI(1:1).

19. The map is entitled: "CARTA MARINA ET DESCRIPTIO SEPTEMTRIONALIVM TERRARVM AC MIRABILIVM RERVM IN EIS CONTENTARVM DILIGENTISME ELABORATA ANNO DŇI 1539 Veneciis . . . Olavs Magnvs. Gotvs. Linkopen." Apparently there were no known survivors of this map until 1886 when a copy was discovered in the Hof-und-Staatsbibliothek, München — now the Bayerische Staatsbibliothek. A second copy came to light in 1962 and was then secured for the Universitetsbibliotek, Uppsala. The map (167x121) was printed on nine sheets. The München copy was first described and reproduced by Brenner(1886)T.15(3:1).

    Reproductions have also been made by Collijn(1912) (3:1) and Klemming(1887) (1:1) on nine sheets. Two of these were reprinted by Kordt(1906)T.2 and 3(each 51x39); and Bagrow(1964)Pl.LXXXII(8:1).

    In 1572, the map was published by Antonio Lafreri in Roma as a copper-engraving on reduced scale (80x53). This edition has been reproduced by Nordenskiöld(1889)59(2:1). On Olaus Magnus, see Bagrow(1930)41-45.

20. For a more extensive treatment of the historical representation of the eastern Baltic coast, see Spekke(1948).

CHAPTER 7: INCREASING PROFESSIONALISM

21. This copybook, or Kollegienbuch, now in the Bayerische Staatsbibliothek, München, has been described in detail by Wolkenhauer(1909). The copybook contains copies of maps from the Ulm edition of Ptolemy, 1486, the Strassburg edition of 1513, and other works of Waldseemüller. For a detailed biography of Münster see Hantzsch(1898); see also Bagrow(1930)1929 and (1964)150-153.

22. This edition of the *Geographia* was republished in facsimile in Theatrvm Orbis Terrarvm, Amsterdam, 1966 as Volume V, 3rd series. In the 1542 edition, the "XV" is replaced by "XX". The 1542 map (34x27) has been reproduced separately by Kordt(1910)T.XX(1:1). The 1540 map(34x27), but with the title "POLONIAE ET VNGARIAE NOVA DESCRIPTIO", is reproduced by Buczek(1966)T.10(6:5).

23. The 1544 map(15^1/$_2$x16^1/$_4$) is reproduced by Nordenskiöld(1889)115(1:1); Kordt(1899)T.VII(1:1), and Bagrow(1918)29(2:1), (1962)44(1:1) and (1964)173(1:1).

    The 1550 map(16^1/$_2$x17^1/$_2$) is reproduced by Kordt(1889)T.VIII(1:1) and Michow(1882-1883)T.1(1:1). The map is thoroughly analysed by Zamýslovski(1880). A small note is included in Kordt(1889)6.

24. The map(16x24) is reproduced here for the first time. Kordt(1899)T.X(1:1) reproduces the same map (but with the title "SARMATIA ASIATICA") from the 1559 Latin edition of the *Cosmographia* which is somewhat imperfect: the names "Don", "Caucasus Mons" and "Euxinus" are missing and the name "Volga Fl." has been turned upside down.

25. Concerning Johannes Honter or Honterus see Bagrow(1928)110-113. The original map (16x12) a wood cut, is reproduced by Michow(1907)T.1(1:1). The second map in Honterus, of Asia, includes the Caspian Sea, the Caucasus and the plains of Sarmatia just to the north.

    Later the wood block of the map of Poland came into the hands of the Basel editor Henrichum Petri and, as an illustration was included in Münster's *Cosmographia* of 1550 and in *Aenei Sylvii Opera*, Basel, 1551, as well. The block was also used in Antwerp in the edition of Honterus(1555) and by Boileau de Bouillon(1555)[Bagrow(1928)45-47]. It is from this book that the reproduction in Michow, mentioned above, has been made.

26. For a brief description of his life — and a complete listing of his works — see Bagrow(1928)74-96. All important literature is indicated there. Of more recent works we may mention Caraci(1936) and Almagià(1939).

27. All of these maps were being reprinted by other editors during the entire 16th-century. Discussions of these reprints can be found in Bagrow(1928)74-96 and in Tooley(1939)16-17. Of the four maps mentioned in the text, reproductions of the following can be seen:

    The 1546 map (53x36) by Grande(1905)T.5(5:2) and in Remarkable Maps(1897)IV,14(1:1). A 1562 reprint of this map(53x29) by Camotius is found in Nordenskiöld(1897)165(3:2).

    The 1548 map (17x12) as included in Ptolemy's *Geographia* with the title "VNIVERSALE NOVO", by Nordenskiöld(1889)T.XLV(1:1) and by Grande(1905)T.3(1:1).

    The 1550 map (77x52) by Bagrow(1928)T.VIII(9:2) and Sykes(1915)T.6(5:1).

    The 1562 map has not as yet been reproduced. See Tooley(1939)16, item 9.

We shall not treat here the question of the Strait of Anian — the supposed passage separating America from Asia, which was mentioned in the descriptive text, published by Pagano in 1562, to a lost world map. Why Gastaldi is credited with initiating this name in uncertain as we have not found any of his maps with this strait; it is possible that the lost world map progressed no further than some final drafting stage. Efforts to explain this name have given rise to a rich literature which is listed in Nunn(1929), Berg(1935) [and its review in *Imago Mvndi*(1939)III] and (1946).

28. The map, a wood cut (73x36) by Matteo Pagano, is without title but includes a descriptive note at the bottom: "La vera descrittione di Tutta la Vngheria: Trasiluania: Valachia: Parte di Polonia: Podollia: e Rossi . . . Per Iacomo de Casteldi Geographo in Venetia D.M. XLVI. Stampata in Venetia per Mattio Pagan in Frezaria al insegnia della Fede". The map was found in the Biblioteca Apostolica Vaticana by R. Almagià who published a facsimile of it(1948)II,T.VI(2:1); also(1934). In Bagrow[(1928)77] an error has been made because at the time of its writing the Dalmation map was not yet known; its title, as described by Gessner, was so unclear that it was easy to link the title to three other maps. See also Almagià(1934).

29. The map of Poland (17x12) has been reproduced by Kordt(1910)T.XXIX(1:1).

     The map of Muscovy (17:13) has been reproduced by Kordt(1899)T.IV(1:1) and Bagrow(1962)42(1:1). The enlarged version (24x18) in Ruscelli's *Geografia* of 1561 is reproduced by Kordt(1899)T.V(1:1).

30. This map, "Descriptione de la Moscouia per Giacomo gastaldo piamotese Cosmographo in Venetia MDL", was engraved on copper (37x26). It was reproduced in Kordt(1899)T.XV(1:1), and by Nordenskiöld(1882)Pl.10(1:1) and in other language editions of this book.

     A copy of this map was published separately in Venezia in 1566 entitled "Noua Descripcione de la Moscovia per l'ecceta N. Giacomo gastaldo piamontese Cosmographo in Venetia Anno MDLXVI Ferando Berteli exc." It is a copper-engraving (38x26). The same year it was also reprinted in Venezia by Camotius. His map has been reproduced by Kordt(1899)T.XVI(1:1) and Remarkable Maps(1897)VI,T.26(1:1). In some editions,,especially those of Lafreri, a few vertical lines have been added to the year, i.e. "MDLXVI IIII".

31. The edition of 1562 is entitled: "Il Disegno de Geografia Moderna Del Regno di Polonia, e parte Del Ducado di Moscouia, conparte della Scandia, parte de Sueuia . . . di castaldi piamotese cosmografo in Venea, MDLXII . . . favio li, °f". [Fabio Licinio]. A copper-engraving (75x52), it was included in many of Lafreri's atlases. Its southern sheet was reproduced by Kordt(1899)T.XXII(7:5).

     The 2nd edition was printed on two sheets as well. However, while only the southern sheet of the first edition carried the title quoted above, each sheet of the 2nd edition has its own heading. The northern sheet is entitled: "A Benigni lettori. Di. M. Iacomo Castaldo ni si rapresenta la prima parte della descriptione del Regno di Polonia, con le sua scala di miglia Intagliata da Paolo furlani ueronese al segno della Colonna. Venetia l'anno. 1568". This sheet (49x37) was reproduced by Kordt(1906)T.VII(1:1) and Nordenskiöld(1889)125(7:3).

     The heading of the southern sheet is: "Il uero disegno della seconda parte dil Regno di Polonia, dell' eccmo mp. Giacomo Gastaldo piamotese. Jn ventia l'Anno MDLXVIII. Jntagliata da Paolo Forlani veronese al segno della Colonna inmerzaria". This sheet (49x37) is in Kordt(1910)T.XXII(1:1) and Bagrow(1917)25(3:1).

32. It had no special title but all of its first sheet is taken up by a framed address to the reader which begins: "Evropam descripturi primum curauimus . . ." The dedication to "D. Antonio Pereenot" is signed . . . "Gerardvs Mercator Rvpelmondanvs Dedicabat". On the lower left sheet: "Absolutum et Diuulgatum est opus Duysburgi anno Dni 1554, mense Octobri, per Gerardum Mercatore Rupelmondanum." The map is a copper-engraving on 15 sheets with a total size of (130x158). The only known copy is in the Biblioteka Uniwersytecka, Wroclaw. It was reproduced by the Gesellschaft für Erdkunde, Berlin(1891)(1:1) and had been described by Heyer(1890)379-390.

     On Mercator and his cartographic work see Bagrow(1930)3-17; Ortroy(1892-93) and (1914-16); Averdunck and Müller-Reinhart(1914); and Aleyner et al.(1962).

33. Brief data about his cartographic work and the principal works of a rich literature on him are given in Bagrow(1928)51-54.

34. The map has come down to us in its manuscript form and is now kept in the British Museum, London, as Plate #123 in the Burghley Atlas. The map (65x31) is signed "William Burowgh". Reproductions are found in Morgan and Coote(1886)II,252(1:1) although (2:1) in the facsimile edition; various other publications of the Hakluyt Society (usually hand drawn); and by Kordt(1906)T.XI(2:1).

     The personal reactions and records of Chancellor, Stephen Burrough, and many of other European travellers to Russia are examined in the two recent works of Wilson(1970) and Haney(1971).

35. For example, it is reprinted in Hakluyt(1903)III,209-212. Gauthier(1937) edits a Russian translation of the passages relating to Russia and Burrough's letter. A considerably reduced reproduction of Burrough's map is appended but is a poor quality photographic reproduction.

36. Ortelius has called it: "RVSSIAE, MOSCOVIAE ET TARTARIAE DESCRIPTIO. Auctore Antonio Ienkensono Anglo, edita Londini Anno. 1562 et dedicata illustriss: D. Henrico Sÿdneo Wallie presidi". The map, a copper-engraving (45x35), has been reproduced by Morgan and Coote(1886)I,cxlviii(1:1) although not in the facsimile edition; Anuchin(1890)256(5:3); Kordt (1899)T.XVII(1:1); Hakluyt(1903)III, Endpiece(1:1); Michow(1910)21(7:5); Bagrow(1914c)9(1:1) and (1917)31; Skelton(1952)T.14(9:4); Wilson(1979)37(3:1); Haney(1971)6 and others.

     In De Jode it is entitled: "MOSCOVIAE MAXIMI AMPLISSIMI QVE DVCATVS chorographica descriptio Authore Anthonio Iankinsono Anglo". This map, also a copper-engraving (24x31), has been reproduced by Malein(1908)328-329(1:1). For information on Jenkinson, see Morgan and Coote(1886); Bagrow(1928)120-121; the various editions of Hakluyt's Voyages; Alekseev(1936)41-48, and Wilson(1970).

37. The complete title of this map is: "REGIONVM SEPTENTRIONALIVM, MOSCOVIAM, RVTENOS, TARTAROS, EORVM-QVE HORDAS CONPREHENDENTIVM, EX ANTONII IENKESONII ET SIGISMVNDI LIBERI BARONIS AB HERBERSTEIN

ITINERARIIS, NOVA DESCRIPTIO." It is a copper-engraving on three sheets(104x50). The only extant copy was in St. Petersburg in the Dashkov collection, but after his death it passed to either the Gosudarstvennaya Publichnaya Bibiloteka imeni M.E. Salt̀y̆kova-Shchedrina, Leningrad or the Gosvdarstvennaya Biblioteka SSSR imeni V.I. Lenina, Moskva. This map has been reproduced and described by Kordt(1906)T.IV-VI(1:1) and Keuning(1956)f.174(3:1).

 Early West European literature evidently has no data about this map. Plantijn's trade-books [see Denucé(1912-13)] mention some maps of Muscovy, of which only one remains unknown to us: a map made in 1573 by the order of Reynold Wolff, the "Schilder" of the British Queen [Denucé(1913)II,25]. It is difficult to tell whether this map was made by Wolff himself or from some already printed map. It is possible that this map was Jenkinson's original map which Ortelius mentions being published in Antwerp.

38.This hand-drawn, colored map (29x39) is kept in the Barberini Library in the Biblioteca Apostolica Vaticana, Roma. It is part of Raphael Barberini's account of his voyage to Moskva in 1564. He was sent there by the Antwerp merchant company for which he obtained from the Tsar the privilege of trading with Moskva by way of Narva. This account and a small copy of the map is printed in Tcharykow(1905). A photocopy of the original is in Michow(1907)T.3(1:1).

39.Grodecki's original map was drafted in Leipzig in 1557 and published in Basel in 1558[Bagrow] or 1562?[Buczek(1963)41] by Jan Oporin. It was cut on four wood blocks at a scale of approximately 1:1,680,000 (78x62). It was long considered lost, but in 1938 Buczek found a copy in the Bayerische Armeebibliothek, Müchen. He was preparing to reproduce it in volume I of *Monumenta Poloniae Cartographica* when this volume was destroyed at the start of the war [Buczek(1966)41]. Postwar efforts to recover the original are related by Modziejowski(1947). Its only reproduction, from the München copy, is by Buczek(1966)T.19(8:3).

 Ortelius included this map in his atlas of 1570 under the title: "POLONIAE finitimarumqve locorum descriptio. Auctore WENCESLAO GODRECCIO. Polono." This map (48x37) has been reproduced by Kordt(1910)T.XXI(1:1).

 In 1589, a copy appeared in Kromer(1589)108(4:3) under the title:"POLONIAE LOCORVEMQVE VICINORVM DE-SCRIPTIO. Auctore Wenceslao Grodeccio Polono". In 1594, it was copied from Ortelius at a reduced scale by Quad(1594)(2:1). Finally, in 1595, Ortelius reprinted his map, adding some supplementary data, under the title: "POLONIAE LITVANIAEQ, DESCRIPTIO. Auctore Wenceslao Godreccio; et correctore Andrea Pograbio Pilsnensi". This map (48x37) is reproduced in Kordt(1910)T.XXIV(1:1). On Grodecki see Buczek(1933c) and (1966)41-44.

 Pograbka produced a two-sheet, copper-engraving (69x46) entitled: "Partis SARMATIAE EVROPEAE . . . NOVA DE-SCRIPTIO." "Andreas Pograbivs Pilsnensis . . . 1569". "Venetsis Nicolas Nelli aereis formis anno dni 1570". Surviving copies are fairly rare. It has been reproduced in Kordt (1899)T.XXIII(1:1) (the eastern sheet); Kordt(1910)T.XXIII(1:1) (the western sheet); Buczek(1966)T.22(2:1), and Almagià(1948)II,T.X.(4:3).

 Strubicz's map(39x32) is entitled: "MAGNI DVCATVS LITHVANIAE LIVONIAE ET MOSCOVIAE DESCRIPTIO." "Matthias Strubicz Nobilis Polonus describebat". It was appended to Kromer(1589)109(1:1) and has been reproduced by Kordt(1910)T.XII(1:1); Buczek(1933b)T.IV(2:1) and (1966)T.26(4:3). Buczek's works contain a great deal of information about other Polish cartographers as well as reproductions of Polish maps. See also Olszewicz(1930) and the catalogue of the exhibition organized on the occasion of the International Geographical Congress, Warsaw, 1934 published by the Bibljoteka Narodowa, Warszawie.

40.Antonisz published his undated woodcut map on nine sheets under the title: "Caerte van oostlant — Antverpiae Per Arnoldum Nicolai" (96x70). His name is signed under the address to the reader. The only known copy of this map is in the Ehemalige Universitätsbibliothek, Helmstedt. It has been reproduced by Björnbo and Petersen(1908)T.5. For information on Antonisz, see Bagrow(1928)27-30.

 Tramezini's map— "SEPTENTRIONALIVM Regionvm. . .Michaelis Tramezini Formis. . .oc DLVIII" — is a copper-engraving (53x38). It was included in the Italian atlasses of Lafreri and others. It is reproduced by Nordenskiöld(1897)T.XXXIV(1:1) and in *Remarkable Maps*(1897)V/VI,T.20(1:1).

 Algoet's original map has not come down to us, but we know a map which was based upon it: "Terrarvm Septentrionalivm Exacta Novissimaqve descriptio per Livinvm Algoet et alijs autoribus 1562. Antuerpie apud Gerardu de Juede supra borsam nonam." This map(99x114) was engraved on copper on six sheets (each 38x33). The only known copy is kept in the Bibliothèque Nationale, Paris. It has been reproduced in Bagrow(1928)T.I-111(4:1). On Algoet's life see Roersch(1910)69-70 and Kordt(1906)12.

41.The map is entitled: "Beschrÿuinge der ZeeCusten van Mezin hem streckende tot het lant van Pitsora dat Eyland Calgoyo mitgaders die principale riviere en hauenen van Ruslant . . . tot Archangel en Calmogro oock eendeel van Corfinlant . . . Door Lucas Ianss Wagenaer tot Enchuysen." The same title is also repeated in French. In subsequent editions, this man was somewhat modified by supplementary information. Kordt(1906)T.IX(1:1) has reproduced the version from the 1596 edition. For information on Waghenaer, see Baart de la Faille(1931) and Belov(1956).

42.Salinghen's map, hand-drawn on parchment (108x86), is entitled: "Rechte Sehe vnde Landt charte der Merengen . . . vnter Degnichsten Dienner Simon van Salinghen jn Coppenhaue Anno 1601." The original, in the Riksarkivets, Stockholm, is in very poor condition. Most of the detailed lettering and the title are now illegible. There is coloring around the coastlines, political boundaries and mountain ranges. The map has been described and reproduced by Björnbo and Petersen(1908)T.X.(2:1); Palmén(1912) (2:1); Richter(1936)T.VI(5:1), and Bagrow(1917)T.39(8:1). The first-named source gives a complete list of the geographical names. On Salinghen's life, see also Kordt(1902)xix-xxix.

43. "Tabula hydrographica, tum maris Baltici (quod Orientale hodie vocant) tum Septentrionalis Oceani nauigationem continens; . . ." The same title in its Dutch version ends with the words ". . . Seer ghebetert doer C.D." and in the upper left hand corner, in a cartouche, "Gedruckt t'Amsterdam by Claes Jamss. Visscher wonende op de Niewesyds Colck Jnde Visscher 1610. Ioannes à Dotecu Baptista à Dotecum Fecerunt". This map, a copper-engraving(40x54), is known only from a copy in the Universitetsbiblioteket, Oslo. It has been reproduced by Wieder(1925)I,T.6(1:1).

44. This edition was handled by another publisher, Cornelis Claesz, who also printed Barents' Mediterranean Atlas. The map of Northern Europe, a copper-engraving (51x33), is entitled, "Hydrographica Septentrionalis Norvegiae partes descriptio in qua quomodo tuto navigare, . . . topographice designatur, a Guil. Barentsono. Petrus Kaerius fecit 1596." The same heading is given in Dutch. Fragments of this map were taken and published separately by Gerrit de Veer in his description of Barents' three expeditions.

45. The map, a copper-engraving (56x41), is entitled: "Deliniato cartae trium navigationum per Batavos, ad Septentrionalem plagam, Norvegiae, Moscoviae, et novae Semblae, et per qB fretum Weygatis Nassovicum dictum . . . Authore Wilhelmo Bernardo Amstelredamo expertissimo pilota." The title in Dutch reads: "Beschryvinghe van de drie Seylagien . . . door WILLEM BARENTS van Amstelredam de vermaerde Piloot." Below in a cartouche: "Auctore Wilhelmo Bernardo. Cornelius Nicolai excudebat. Baptista a' Doetechum schulp. A° 1598". The map has been reproduced by Kordt(1906)T.X.(1:1); Skelton(1952)T.30(9:4); Muller(1878)T.19(1:1); Michow(1910)(5:3); L'Honore Naber(1917)XV(1:1);Bagrow(1964)169(3:1); Yefimov(1964)T.23(2:1); and in several of the volumes of the Hakluyt Society.

   The reduced copy of the map(35x26) was included in *Rerum et urbis Amstelodamensium historia* prepared by J. Pontanus and published by Jod. Hondius in 1611. This map is entitled "TABULA GEOGR. in qua admirandae navigationis cursus et recursus designature." This map has been reproduced by Asher(1860)(1:1); de Bas(1878)1(1:1); Nordenskiöld(1882)Pl.5(5:4);and Belov(1956)f.80(4:3). A brief note on Barents can be found in Vizye(1948a).

46. The account of Barents' expeditions prepared by de Veer first appeared in print in 1598 in Dutch, Latin, French and German editions. The maps and plans attached to it were:
   1. From North Cape to Novaya Zemlya, with a separate plan to Loms Bay, (22x14).
   2. Yugorskiy Shar (21x14).
   3. "Caerte van Nova Zembla, de Weygats, de custe van Tartarien en Ruslandt tot Kilduyn toe, . . . Door Gerrit de Veer beschreven. Baptista a Doetechum Sculp. a°, 1598."(25x18).
   4. The Lapland coast from Kegor to the Svyatoy Cape (21x14).
   5. The Kola Bay and the island of Kildin (20x14).
   All these maps, plus plans and illustrations, are reproduced at various sizes by L'Honoré Naber(1917)XIV,K.I-V, and in various editions of the Hakluyt Society. Map number 3, Caerte van Nova Zembla, has also been reproduced by Kordt(1906)T.XXIV(1:1).

47. The large map carries the title: "EVROPAM ab Asia & Africa, segregant Mare, mediterraneium . . ." (40x56). The map is anonymous except for the engraver's name— "Baptista à Doetecum fecit." It would seem, however, that this map is a work of Peter Plancius and was prepared with some others for some special publication. See Burger(1915a)415 and 418. The small map (9x13) has its own title: "DESCRIPTIO NOVAE ZEMBLAE, at quam penitius cognoscenda, mense Iulio proximè elapso presentis anni 1594 . . ." It has been reproduced by Burger(1915a)419(1:1) and (1915b)325(1:1).

48. This edition appeared in Antwerp under the title: "Europae primae et potissimae tertiae partes descriptio . . . Caspare Vopelio Medebach Mathematico Authore. B. van den putte MDLXVI." A woodcut on nine full sheets (each 33x43) and three half-sheets (each 19x34). A fragmentary copy is in the Bibliothèque Nationale, Paris. Its northeastern corner, which relates to Russia, has been reproduced by Michow(1907)T.4(1:1). Other later editions of this map have also come down to us. About them and about Vopel in general see Bagrow(1930)96-97; Michow(1892); and Koch(1937).

49. The world map of 1569 is entitled: "NOVA ET AVCTA ORBIS TERRAE DESCRIPTIO AD VSVM NAuigantium emendate accomodata. Aeditum autem est opus hoc Duysburgi an: D.1569 mense Augusto". The dedication to Duke Johann Wilhem of Kleve is signed "Gerardus Mercator". It is a copper-engraving on eighteen sheets (total size 134x212). The sheets which embrace Russia and northern Asia are Nos. V and VI of the upper row and Nos. XI and XII of the middle row. Copies of this map are kept in the Bibljoteka Uniwersytecka, Wroclaw; Oeffentliche Bibliothek der Universität Basel, Basel; Bibliothèque Nationale , Paris;Maritiem Museum"*Prins Hendrik*",Rotterdam; and in the private collection of *Count Mirbach*.

   The copy in Rotterdam was only recently found in Holland and nteresting and peculiar among them. It is made in the form of an atlas for convenient use while at sea. It consists of 29 sheets. To make this atlas, three copies of the map were needed. The Wroclaw copy has been published in facsimile by the *Gesellschaft für Erkunde*, Berlin(1891)(1:1). Another reproduction was published in Monaco by the Bureau Hydrographique International together with an English translation of the legend of the map [(Anonymous(1932a)]. A somewhat less perfect reproduction is given by Jomard(1842-62)T.XXI.1-XXI.8; Taylor(1955)104(4:1); and Bagrow(1964)Pl.LXX(10.1). For other reprints of this map see Bagrow(1930)9-10. For the posthumus edition(1595) and later editions of Mercator's atlas, this map was reworked into a number of separate maps of the world, Asia, Africa, America, and the Arctic regions.

50. The map of Europe of 1572 is entitled: "Evropae descriptio emendata anno MDLXXII. Absolutum et eullgatum est opus Duisburgi anno Dni 1554, mense Octobri, per Gearadum Mercator Rupelmondanum. Et iterum ibidem emendatum Dni 1572, mense Martio," It was printed on 15 sheets (total size 134x160). Copies of this map are in the Oeffentliche Bibliothek der

Universität Basel, Basel; Thüringische Landesbibliothek, Weimar; and Biblioteca Civica, Perugia. This map has not been reproduced in total. Only those parts relating to Russia have been reproduced by Michow(1907)T.5 (with a brief description) and Bagrow(1917)34 from Michow.

51. The atlas included the following maps:
    (a) "Rvssia cum confinijs . . . per Gerardum Mercatorem" (47x35) with an inset map "Rvssiae pars Amplificata"(14x12). They have been reproduced by Kordt(1899)T.XXIV(1:1) and Bagrow(1917)35(3:1). The inset alone has been reprinted by Buczek(1933b)T.VI(1:1).
    (b) "Livonia per Gerardum Mercatorem" (47x36).
    (c) "Lithvania — Per Gerardum Mercatorem" (44x37). It has been reproduced by Kordt(1910)T.X (1:1); Buczek(1933b)T.V(2:1); and the upper part only, Buczek(1966)T.27(1:1).
    (d) "Tavrica Chersonesvs. Nostra aetate Przecopsca et Gazra dicitur . . . Per Gerardum Mercatorem" (40x31). It is reproduced in Kordt(1910)T.XI(1:1).
    (e) Polonia et Silesia. Per Gerardum Mercatorem" (45x34). Reproduced in Buczek(1933b)T.II(2:1) and Buczek(1966)T.23(3:2).
    (f) "Septentrionalvm terrarum descriptio per G. Mercatorem" (36x39).

52. This map — "Moscoviae totivs cvm regionibvs finitimis descriptio" — was a coarse woodcut (34x40). It has been reproduced by Kordt(1899)T.28(1:1).

53. "Moscoviae Imperivm" — (17x12) — reproduced by Kordt(1899)T.XXV(1:1). A copy was included in several publications of Matthias Quad. An engraving (28x21) by Ja. Bussemecher in 1600 has been reproduced by Kordt(1899)T.XXVII(1:1).

BIBLIOGRAPHY

Adelung, Friedrich von (1818). *Siegmund Freiherr von Herberstein. Mit besonderer Ruecksicht auf seine Reisen in Russland . . . St. Petersburg: N. Gretsch. 513 pp.*

Alekseyev, Mikhael Pavlovich (1932). *Sibir' v izvestiyakh zapadnoevropeyskikh puteshestvennikov i pisateley* [Siberia in the Writings of Western European Travellers and Writers]. Irkutsk: Kraygiz, Vol. I, Part 1.

——————— (1936). Vol. 1, Part 2.

Alekseyev, V. (1936). *Istoricheskiye puteshestviya* [Historic Journeys]. Stalingrad: Krayevoye Knigoizdatel'stvo.

Aleyner et al. (1962). = Aleyner, A.Z., Larionova, A.N., i Churkin, V.G., *Gerard Merkator 450 let so dnya pozhdeniya* [Gerard Mercator, 450 Years Since His Birth]. Moskva: Gosudarstvennoye Izd. Geog. Lit. 79 pp.

Almagià, Roberto (1934). "Sulle carte della Polonia di Giacomo Gastaldi", *Zbior Prac Poswiecony przez towarzystwo Geograficne we Lwowie Eugenjuszowi Romerowi w 40-lecie jego Tworczosci Naukowj*, 143-148.

——————— (1944, 1948, 1952, 1955). *Monumenta Cartographica Vaticana*. Città del Vaticana: Bibliotheca Apostolica Vaticana. 4 Vols.

Almagià, Roberto and Marcel Destombes. (1964). *Monumenta Cartographica Vetustioris aevi A.D. 1200-1500*. Vol I — Mappaemundi. Amsterdam: N. Israel.

Andreyevskiy, I. (1863). "Razskaz Rimsko-katolicheskago missionera Domikantsa Yuliana, o puteschestvii v strany privolzhskikh Vengertsev, sovershennom pered 1235 godom . . ." [The Story of the Roman Catholic Missionary Domikants Julian, About the Journey to the Country of the Unconquered Hungarians Completed before 1235 . . .] *Odesskoye Obshchestvo Istorii i Drevnostey, Zapiski*, V, 998-1010.

Anonimov, Ivan Nikolaevich (trans.). (1866). *Zapiski o Moskoviy (Rerum moscoviticarum commentarii) Barona Herbershteyna* [Notes on Muscovy by Baron Herberstein]. St. Petersburg: Tip. V. Bezobrazova i Komp.

Anonymous (1932a). "Text and Translation of the Legends of the Original Chart of the World by Gerhard Mercator Issued in 1569", *Hydrographic Review*, IX, 7-45.

Antonovich, V. B. (1900). *Arkheologicheskaya karta Volynskoy gubernii* [Archaeological Map of the Volynskaya Province]. Moskva: Tip. G. Lissnera i A. Geshelya.

Anuchin, D. N. (1890). "K istorii oznakomleniya s Sibir'yu do Yermaka" [Concerning History of Knowledge of Siberia Before Yermak], *Moskovskoye Arkheologicheskoye Obshchestvo, Drevnosti*, XIV, 227-313.

——————— . (1895). "Rel'yef poverkhnosti Yevropicheskoy Rossii v posledovatel'nom razvitiy o nem predstav-leniy" [Relief of the Surface of European Russia in Consecutively Developed Representation], *Zemlevedniye*, I, 77-126.

Arkas, Z. (1853). "Sravnitel'naya tablitsa Ėllinskikh poseleniy po Yevksinskomu Pontu . . ." [Comparative Table of Hellenic Colonies on the Black Sea], *Odesskoye Obshchestvo Istorii i Drevnostey, Zapiski*, III, 144-150.

Asher, George Michael. (1860). *Henry Hudson the Navigator*. London: The Hakluyt Society. No. XXVII.

Atlas Russicus . . . (1745). St. Petersburg: Academiae Imperialis Scientiarum.

Averdunck, H. & Müller-Reinhart, J. (1914). "Gerhard Mercator und die Geographen unter seinen Nachkommen," *Petermanns Mitteilungen, aus Justus Perthes' Geographischer Anstalt*, Ergänzungsband XXXIX, (182), 1.188.

Baart de la Faille, R. D. (1931). "Nieuwe gegevens over Lucas Jansz. Wagenaer," *Het Boek*, XX (May), 145-160.

Baddely, John F. (1919). *Russia, Mongolia, China*. London: MacMillan and Co. 2 Vols.

——————— *Facsimile edition*. New York: Burt Franklin, 1964.

Bagdasarijan, A. B. and Yeremyan, S. T. (1968). "Geografiya i kartografiya v Armenii v V-VIIv.v." [Geography and Cartography in Armenia in the 5-7th C.], *Sovetskiye Geografiya na XXI Mezdunarodnomu Geograficheskomu Kongressu*, 132-133.

Bagrow, Leo. (1912a). "Materialy k istoricheskomu obzory kart Kaspiyskago Morya" [Materials for an Historical Survey of the Maps of the Caspian Sea], *Glavnoye Gidrograficheskoye Upravleniye, Morskago Ministerstva: Zapiski po Gidrografii*, XXXV, 1-112.

——————— . (1914a). *Drevniye karty Chernago Morya* [Early Maps of the Black Sea]. St. Petersburg.

——————— . (1914c). "Kartografiya Aziatskoy Rossii" [Cartography of Asiatic Russia], *Atlas Aziatskoy Rossii*. St. Petersburg: A. F. Marks. pp. 1-4.

——————— . (1917). *Istoriya geograficheskoy karty. Ocherk i ukazatel' literatury* [The History of the Geographical Map. Review and Survey of the Literature]. Petrograd:

——————— . (1918). "Istoriya geograficheskoy karty" [The History of the Geographical Map], *Arkheologicheskiy Institut, St. Petersburg, Vestnik Arkheologii i Istorii*, XXIII, 1-136.

——————— . (1928). "A. Ortelli Catalogus Cartographorum," part one, *Petermanns Mitteilungen, aus Justus Perthes' Geographischer Anstalt*, Ergänzungsband XLII (199), 5-137.

——————— . (1930). "A. Ortelli . . . ," part two, *Petermanns Mitteilungen, aus Justus Perthes' Geographischer Anstalt*, Ergänzungsband XLV (210), 1-122.

——————. (1932). "Die Manuskript-Atlanten des Battista Agnese," *Petermanns Mitteilungen, aus Justus Perthes' Geographischer Anstalt*, LXXVIII (Heft 7/8), 190-191.

——————. (1935). *Die ersten Karten der Ukraine (XVII Jh.)*. *Anectoda Cartographica, I*. Berlin: Verlage der Gesellschaft der Freunde des Ukrainischen Wissenschaftlichen Institutes.

——————. (1939b). *Giovanni Andreas di Vavassore, a Venetian Cartographer of the 16th century. A Descriptive List of His Maps*. Jenkintown, Pa.: The George H. Beans Library. Publication No. 14.

——————. (1945). "The Origin of Ptolemy's Geographia," *Geografiska Annaler*, XXVII, 318-387.

——————. (1956a). "Italians on the Caspian," *Imago Mundi*, XIII, 3-10.

——————. (1962). "At the Sources of the Cartography of Russia," *Imago Mundi*, XVI, 33-48

——————. (1964). *History of Cartography*, ed. R. A. Skelton. Cambridge: Harvard U. Press.

Barentz, Willem (1595). *Nieuwe Beschryvinghe ende Caert Baeck Vande Midlandtsche Zee*. Amstelredam: Cornelis Claesz.

Belov, Mikhail Ivanovich. (1956). *Arkticheskoye moreplavaniye s drevneyshikh vremen do serediny XIX veka* [Arctic Sea-Expeditions from Earliest Times Until the Middle of the XIXth Century]. Vol. I of *Istoriya otkrytiya i osvoyeniya severnogo morskogo puti*. Moskva: Izdatel'stvo Morskoy Transport.

Berchet, Guglielmo. (1880). *Il planisfero di Giovanni Leardo dell'Anno 1452*. Venezia: Ferd. Ongania.

Berg, L. S. (1935). *Otkrytiye Kamchatki i ekspeditsii Beringa* [The Explorations of Kamchatka and the Expeditions of Bering]. Leningrad: Izdatel'stvo Glavsemorputi.

——————. (1946). *Otkrytiye Kamchatki i ekspeditsii Beringa 1725-1742* [The Explorations of Kamchatka and the Expeditions of Bering, 1725-1742]. 3d ed.; Moskva-Leningrad: Izdatel'stvo AN SSSR.

Biasutti, Renato. (1941). "E stata ritrovata a Firenze la carta navigatoria di Paolo dal Pozzo Toscanelli?," *Rivista Geographica Italiana*, XLVIII, 293-301.

Birkenmajer, Ludwik Antoni. (1901). "Marco Beneventano Kopernik, Wapowski, a najstarsza Karta geograficzna Polski," *Polska Akademja Umiejętności*, Serya III, I, dzial A, Ogolnego zbioru XLI, 134-222.

Bjornbo, A. A. & Peterson, C. S. (1908). *Anedtoda Cartographica Septentrionelia*. Hauniae: Sumptius Societatis Regiae Scientarium Danicae.

Blau, M. (1835). "Mémoire sur deux monuments géographiques conservés à la bibliothèque publique de Nancy," *Société Royale des Sciences, Lettres et Arts de Nancy, Memoires*, LIII-LXIV, and *Supplément du Memoires*, 67-105.

Boileau de Bouillon, Gilles. (1555). *La Spère des deux mondes, composée en français par Darimal, pasteur des Amadis . . .* Anvers: J. Richart.

Bongars, (1611). *Gesta dei per Francos . . .* Hanoviae.

Borisov, V. (1909-1911). "Karta Sarmatii (nyneshney Rossii) vo II veke po R.Kh. po grecheskomu geografu Ptolomeyu" [The Map of Sarmatia According to the Greek Geography of Ptolemy], *Materialy dlya sostavleniya karty*, 3 vols. This citation never verified by the editor.

Braun, F. (1899). "Razyskaniya v oblasti goto-slavyanskikh otnosheniy" [Discoveries in the Sphere of Gotho-Slavonic Relations], *Akademiya Nauk, Otdeleniye Russkago Yazyka i Slovesnosti, Sbornik*, LXIV (#12), 1-392.

Brenner, Oscar. (1886). "Die ächte Karte des Olaus Magnus vom Jahre 1539, nach dem Exemplar der Münchener Staatsbibliothek," *Christiania Videnskabs: Selskabs Forhandlunger*, No. 15.

Brown, Lloyd A. (1949). *The Story of Maps*. Boston: Little, Brown and Co,

Brutzkus, Yulii Davidovich. (1924). *Pis'mo Khazarskogo Yevreya ot X veka* [A Letter from a Khazar Jew of the 10th Century]. Berlin.

Buchon, J. A. C. & Tastu, J. (1839). "Notice d'un Atlas en langue Catalane, manuscrit de l'an 1375 . . . ," *Notices et Extraits des Manuscrits de la Bibliothèque du Roi*, XIV, 1-153.

Buczek, Karol. (1933b). "Kartografia Polska w czasach Stefana Batorego," *Wiadomości Sluzby Geograficznej*, VII (#2), 62-118.

——————. (133c). "Waclaw Grodecki," *Polski Przeglad Kartograficzny*, Vol VI, Rok. XI (#43), 69-86.

——————. (1963). *Dzieje Kartografii Polskiej od XV do XVIII wieku*. Warszawa: Zaklad narodowy imiena ossolinskich wydanistwo Polskiej akademii nauk.

——————. (1966). *The History of Polish Cartography*, trans. Andrzej Potocki. Warszawa: Zaklad Narodowy imienia ossolinskich Wydawnictwo Polskiej Akademii Nauk.

Burger, Cumbertus Pieter. (1900, 1907, 1910, 1915a). *De Amsterdamsche Boekdrukkers en Uitgevers in de Zestiende Eeuw*. Amsterdam: C. L. van Langenhuysen. (Vols. I-III) 'S. Gravenhage: Martin Nijhof. (Vol. IV)

——————. (1915b). "De noordpoolstreken op onze 16 eeuwsche Kaarten," *Het Boek*, IV, part 1: 209-216, part 2: 260-267, part 3: 318-325, part 4: 377-384.

Canale, Michele Giuseppe. (1855). *Della Crimea, del suo commercio e dei suoi dominatori, dalle origini fino ai di nostri*. Genova: Tipi de'Sordomuti. 3 Vols.

Caraci, Giuseppe. (1936). "Note critiche sui mappamondi Gastaldini," *Rivista Geografica Italiana, Roma,* XLIII (#3-4), 120-137; XLII (#5), 202-223.

Choix de documents géographiques conservés à la Bibliothèque Nationale. Paris.

Chowaniec, Czeslaw. (1955). "The First Geographical Map of Bernard Wapowsky," *Imago Mundi,* XII, 59-64.

Collijn, Isak Gustaf Alfred. (1539). *Olaus Magnus Gothus. Ain kurze Auslegung der neuen mappen von den alten Goettenreich und andern Nordlenden.* Venedig.

Crinò, S. (1941). "La scoperta della carta originale di Paolo dal Pozzo Toscanelli che servi di guida a Cristofaro Columbo per il viaggio verso il Nuovo Mondo," *L'Universo,* XXII, 379-410.

Crivellari, Giuseppe. (1903). *Alcuni cimeli della cartografia Medievale esistenti a Verona.* Firenze: B. Seeber.

Crone, Gerald Roe (ed.). (1948a). *The Hereford World Map.* London: Royal Geographical Society.

——————. (1948b). "The Hereford World Map, circa 1290," *Imago Mundi,* V, 14.

——————. (1965). "New Light on the Hereford Map," *Geographical Journal,* CXXXI (#4, Dec.), 447-462.

Cumont, Franz Valéry Marie. (1925a). "Un extrait d'une carte romaine d'état-major," *La Géographie, revue mensuelle,* XLIII (#1, Jan.), 1-5.

——————. (1925b). "Fragment de Bouclier Portant une Liste d'Etapes," *Syria, Revue d'art Oriental et d'archéologie,* VI, 1-15.

——————. (1926a). "Fouilles de Doura-Europas (1922-1923)," *Bibliothèque Archéologique et Historique, Paris,* IX.

de Bas, F. (1878). "Het Doopregister van Spitsbergen," *Nederlandsch Aardijkskondig Genootschap, Amsterdam: Tijdschrift,* III, 1-30.

Denucé, Jean. (1912-1913). *Oud-Nederlandsche Kaartmakers in betrekking met Plantijn.* Antwerpen: De Nederlandsche Boekhandel. 2 vols.

——————. *Facsimile edition.* Amsterdam: Meridian Publishing Co., 1964.

Desimoni, Cornelio. (1893). "Una carta della Terra Santa del secolo XIV nell'Archivio di stato in Firenze. Marino Sanuto e Pietro Visconte," *Archivo Storico Italiano,* X, 241-258.

Durazzo, P. (1885). *Il planisfero di Giovanni Leardo. Con facsimile in cromolitografia e quattro tavole incise.* Mantova: Eredi Segna.

Eckmann, J. (1929). "Keleteuropa es nyugatázsia a legrégibb arab terkepen," *Société Hongroise de Géographie, Budapest,* LVII, 91-105.

Fischer, Joseph. (1915). "Die Entdeckung Russland durch Nikolaus Poppel in den Jahren 1486-1489," *Stimmen der Zeit; Katholische Monatschrift für das Geistesleben der Gegenwart,* LXXXIX, 395-400.

——————. (1916a). "Der russische Zar als "Kaiser" auf der Carta Marina Waldseemüllers vom Jahre 1516." *Stimmen der Zeit; Katholische Monatschrift für das Geistesleben der Gegenwart,* XC, 108-116.

——————. (1916b). "Ptolemäus und Agathodämon," *Akademie der Wissenschaften zu Wien, Philosophisch-Historische Klasse: Denkschriften,* LIX (Abhandlung 4, Anhang II), 69-93.

——————. (1918). "Der Nürnberger Arzt Dr. Hieronymus Münzer († 1508) aus Feldkirch als Mensch und als Gelehrter," *Stimmen der Zeit; Katholische Monatschrift für das Geistesleben der Gegenwart,* XCII, 148-168.

——————. (1930). "Die Karte des Nicolaus von Cusa (vor 1490), die älteste Karte von Mitteleuropa," *Deutsche Universität, Prague, Geographisches Institut: Kartographische Denkmäler der Sudetenländer,* I.

——————. (1932). *Claudii Ptolemaei Geographiae Codex Urbinas Graecus 82.* Leipzig: Ottonem Harrassowitz. 4 vols.

Fischer, Joseph, & Wieser, v. Fr. (1903). *Die älteste Karte mit dem Namen Amerika aus dem Jahre 1507 und die Carta Marina aus dem Jahre 1516 des M. Waldseemüller (Ilacomilus).* Insbrück; Wagner.

——————. *Facsimile edition.* Amsterdam: Theatrum Orbis Terrarum, 1968.

Fischer, Theobald. (1886). *Sammlung Mittelalterlicher Welt-und Seekarten italienischen Ursprungs . . .* Venedig: Ferdinand Ongania.

——————. *Facsimile edition.* Amsterdam: Meridian Publishing Co., 1961.

Formaleoni, Vincenzio Antonio. (1788). *Essai sur la marine ancienne des Vénitiens . . . .*Venetzia.

Fren, Khristian Danilovich (trans.). (1823). *Ibn Forzlana [sic] i drugikh aravityan izvestiya o russakh drevneishikh vremyon* [Ibn Fadlan and Other Arabian Information on Ancient Russian Times]. St. Petersburg: Akademiya Nauk. This citation never verified by the editor.

Freytag Drabbe, von. (1938). "Die Peutingertafel," *Comptes Rendus,* I, *Actes du Congrès,* 422-427. Amsterdam: Congrès International de Géographie.

Gasparrini Leprace, Tullia (ed.). (1956). *Il mappamondo di Fra Mauro.* Roma: Instituto poligrafico dello Stato, Libreria dello Stato.

Gautier, Yurii Vladimirovich. (1937). *Angliiskiye puteshestvenniki v Moskovskom Gosudarstve v XVi veke* [An English Traveller in the Moscow State in the 16th Century]. Leningrad. This citation never verified by the editor.

Gesellschaft für Erdkunde, Berlin. (1891). *Drei Karten von Gerhard Mercator: Europa, Britische Inseln, Weltkarte.* Berlin.

Gessner, Konrad. (1548). *Pandectarum Libri.*

—————. (1551). *Historiae Animalium.* Zürich.

Giovio, Paolo. (1525). *Nuvocomensis libellus de legatione Basilii magni Principis Moschouiae ad Clementem VII . . .* Roma.

Goldschmidt, E. P. (1938). "Hieronymus Münzer und seine Bibliothek," *London University, The Warburg Institute: Studies,* IV, 1-154.

Grande, Stefano. (1905). *Le Carte d'America di Giacomo Gastaldi: . . .*Torino: Carlo Clausen.

Günther, Siegmund. (1896). "Jacob Ziegler, ein bayerischer Geograph und Mathematiker," *Forschungen zur Kultur-und Litteraturgeschite Bayerns,* IV, 1-61.

—————. (1897). "Studien zu Jacob Zieglers Biographie," *Forschungen zur Kultur-und Litteraturgeschite Bayerns,* V, 116-128.

Hakki, Ibrahim. (1936). *Topkapi Saraynda: Deri Uzerine Yapilmis eski' Haritalar.* Istanbul.

Hakluyt, Richard. (1598-1600). *The Principal Navigations, Voyages, Traffiques and Discoveries of the English Nation.* London: George Bishop, Ralph Newberrie and Robert Barker. 3 Vol.

Hallberg, Ivar. (1906). *L'Extrême Orient dans la littérature et la cartographie de l'Occident des XIIIe, XIVe et XVe siècles.* Göteborg: Wald. Zachrissons Boktryckeri A.B.

Hamy, E. T. (1886). "La Mappemonde d'Angelino Dulcert, de Majorque (1339)," *Bulletin de Géographie Historique et Descriptive,* I, 354-366.

—————. *Facsimile edition. Acta Cartographica,* III (1968), 36-48.

—————. (1891). "Cresques lo Juheu. Note sur un géographe Juif Catalan de la fin du XIVe siècle," *Bulletin de Géographie Historique et Descriptive,* VI, 218-222.

—————. *Facsimile edition. Acta Cartographica,* VI (1969), 169-173.

—————. (1903).*La Mappemonde d'Angelino Dulcert, de Majorque (1339).*Paris: Honore Champion.

Haney, Barbara Mary (1971). "*Western Reflections of Russia 1517-1812,*" Unpublished Ph.D. Dissertation, University of Washington.

Hantzsch, Viktor. (1898). "Sebastian Münster: Leben, Werk, wissenschaftliche Bedeutung," *Sächsische Gesellschaft der Wissenschaften, Leipzig, Philologisch-Historische Klasse: Abhandlungen,* XVIII (#3), 1-187.

—————. *Facsimile edition.* Nieuwkoop: B. de Graff, 1965.

Harkavy, A. Ya. (1870). *Skazaniya musul'manskikh pisateley o slavyanakh i russkikh (s Poloviny VII yeka do Kontsa X veka po R. kh.)* [Muslim Writer's Legends on the Slavonians and Russians (from the Middle of the VIIth Century to the End of the Xth)]. Sanktpeterburg: Tip. Imp. Akad. Nauk.

—————. (1874).*Skazaniya yevreyskikh pisateley khazarakh i khazarskom tsarstve* [Jewish Writer's Legends on the Khazars and the Khazar Kingdom]. St. Petersburg: Tip. Imp. Akad. Nauk.

Henne-am-Rhyn, Otto. (1903). *Deutsche Kulturgeschishte.* Berlin.

Herrmann, Albert. (1935). "Die älteste türkische Weltkarte (1706 nach Chr.)," *Imago Mundi,* I, 21-28.

—————. (1940). *Die ältesten Karten con Deutschland bis Gerhard Mercator.* Leipzig: K. S. Koehler Verlag.

Heyd, Wilhelm von. (1879). *Geschichte des Levantehandels in Mittelalter.* Stuttgart.

Heyer, Alfons von. (1890). "Drei Mercator-Karten in der Breslauer Stadt-Bibliothek," *Zeitschrift für Wissenschaftliche Geographie, Weimar,* VII, 379-389, 474-487, 507-528.

—————. *Facsimile edition. Acta Cartographica,* I (1967). 215-262.

Hildebrabd, Hans. (1878). "Ett geografiskt arbete öfver Skandinavien fran ar 1532," *Svenska Sällskapet för Anthropologi och Geografi, Skrifter; Geografiska Sektion, Tidskrift,* I(#2), 1-72.

Hinks, A. R. (1929). *The Portolan Chart of Angellino de Dalorto MCCCXXV in the collection of Prince Corsini at Florence.* London: Royal Geographical Society.

Honterus, Johannes. (1542). *Rudimenta Cosmographica.* Transylvania.

Jaubert, Amédée. (1836, 1840). "Géographie d'Edrisi," *Société de Géographie, Paris: Recueil des Voyages et de Mémoires,* V, VI.

Jomard, Edmé Francois. (1842-1862). *Les Monuments de la Géographie, ou Recueil d'Anciennes Cartes Européennes et Orientales . . . en Fac-simile de la Grandeur des Originaux.* Paris: M. D'avezac. 8 Vols.

Keuning, J. (1956). "The Van Langren Family," *Imago Mundi,* XIII, 101-109.

Khasanov, Kh. (1964). "Nerasshifrovannaya nadpis' na karte Makhmuda kashgarskogo" [An Undeciphered Inscription on the 11th C. Map of Mahmud of Kashgar], *Akademiya Nauk, Izvestiya, Seriya Geograficheskaya,*(#6), 107-108.

Khvol'son, D. A. (1869). *Izvestiya o Khozarakh, Burtasakh, Bolgarakh, Mad'yarakh, Slavyanakh, i Russakh Ibn-Dasta* [Information on the Khazars, Burtas, Bulgars, Magyars, Slavonians, and Russians by Ibn-Dustah] *Izdal, perevel, i ob''yasnil D. A. Khvol'son* [Published in translation with explanations by D. A. Khvol'son].

Kimble, George Herbert. (1934). *The Catalan World Map of the R. Biblioteca Estense at Modena.* London: Royal Geographical Society.

——————. (1935). "The Laurentian World Map with Special Reference to its Portrayal of Africa," *Imago Mundi*, I, 29-33.

Klemming, Gustav Edvard. (1887). *Generalstabens Litografiska Anstalt*. Stockholm. This citation not verified by the editor.

Koch, Herbert. (1937). "Caspar Vopelius, Kartograph in Köln 1511 bis 1561," *Familiengeschichtliche Blätter, Deutscher Herold*, 256.

Kordt, V. (1899, 1906 & 1910). *Materialy po russkoy Kartografii* [Materials on Russian Cartography]. Kiev: Izdatel'stvo Kievskoy Kommissii dlya razbora drevnikh aktov.

——————. (1902)."Ocherk snosheniy Moskovskago Gosudarstva a respublikoyu Soyedinennykh Niderlandov do 1631 g." [An Essay of the Relations of the Moscow State With the Republic of the United Netherlands Before 1631], *Russkoye Istoricreskoye Obshchestvo, Sbornik*, CXVI.

——————. (1931). *Materialy do istorii kartografii Ukraini* [Materials on the History of Ukranian Cartography]. Kiev: Vseukrains'ka Akademiya Nauk Arkheografichna Komisiya.

Kovalevskiy, A. P. (1956). *Kniga Akhmeda Ibn-Fadlana o yego puteshestvii na Volgy v 921-922 gg; stat'i, perevody, i kommentarii* [Akhmed Ibn-Fadlan's Book on His Journey to the Volga in 921-922; Articles, Translations and Commentaries]. Kharkhov: Izdatel'stvo Khar'kovskogo ordema trudovogo krasnogo znameni gos. univ. im. A. M. Gor'kogo.

Krachkovskiy, I. Yu. (1937). "Arabskiye geografy i puteshestvenniki" [Arabian Geographers and Travellers], *Gosudarstvennoye Russkoye Geograficheskoye Obshchestvo, Izvestiya*, LXIX (#5). 738-765.

Kretschmer, Konrad. (1891a). "Marino Saundo der ältere und die Karten des Petrus Vesconte," *Gesellschaft für Erdkunde zu Berlin: Zeitschrift*, XXVI, 352-370.
Facsimile edition. Acta Cartographica, VII (1970), 217-239.

——————(1891b). "Eine neue mittelalterliche Weltkarte der vatikanischen Bibliothek," *Gesellschaft für Erdkunde zu Berlin' Zeitschrift*, XXVI, 371-406.
Facsimile edition. Acta Cartographica, VI (1969), 237-272.

——————(1897). "Die Katalanische Weltkarte der Biblioteca Estense zu Moderna," *Gesellschaft für Erdkunde zu Berlin: Zeitschrift*, XXXII, 65-111,191-218.
Facsimile edition. Acta Cartographica, II (1968), 358-432, part I only.

——————(1909). "Die italienischen Portlane des Mittelalter," *Berlin Universität, Institut für Meereskunde*, XIII.

Kromer, Marcin. (1589).*Martini Cromeri Varmiensis Episcopi Polonia: . . .*Coloniae Agrippinae.

Kubitschek, Wilhelm. (1934). "Studien zur Geographie des Ptolemäus. I. Das Netz der Grenzpunkte," *Akademie der Wissenschaften, Wien, Philosophisch-Historische Klasse: Anzeiger*, LXXI, 75-87.

——————(1935a). "Studien zue Geographie des Ptolemäus. I. Die Ländergrenzen," *Akademie der Wissenschaften, Wien, Philosophisch-Historische Klasse: Sitzungsberichte*, CCXV (Ahandlung 5), 1-161.

Kulakovskiy, Yulian Andreyevich. (1899a). "Novyya dannyya dlya istorii Starago Kryma" [New Facts About the History of the Old Crimea], *Russkoye Arkheologicheskoye Obshchestvo, Zapiski, Novaya Seriya*, X (#3), 1-13.

——————(1899b). "*Karta evropeiskoy Sarmatii po Ptolemeyu . . .*" [Ptolemy's Map of European Sarmatia]. Kiev: Tip. S. V. Kul'zhenko.

——————(1914). *Proshloye Tavridy. Kratkiy istoricheskiy Ocherk* [Tavrida's Past. A Short Historical Essay]. Kiev: S. V. Kul'zhenko. 2nd ed. rev.

Kunik, Arist Aristovich. (1878) (1903). *Izvestia Al-Bekri in drugikh avtorov o Rusi i Slavyanakh* [Information Given by al-Bekri and Others on the Rus and the Slavonians], trans. V. Rozen. St. Petersburg: Akademiya Nauk. 2 parts.

La Espada, Marcos Jiménez De. (1877). "El libro del conocimiento de todas los Reinos, Tierras y Señoríos que son por el Mundo, que escribió un franciscano español á mediados del Siglo XIV, . . . ," *Sociedad Geografica Nacional, Madrid: Boletin*, II (Jan.), 7-66, II (Feb.), 91-141, III (Mar.), 185-210.

Langlois, Victor. (1867). *Géographie de Ptolemee*. Paris: L'Institut et de la Marine.

La Ronciere, Charles de. (1924, 1925, 1927). "La Découverte de l'Afrique au Moyen Age, "Cartographes et Explorateurs," *Société Royale de Géographie d'Egypte, Cairo: Mémoires*, V, 1-174; VI, 1-139; XIII, 1-105.

Latyshev, Vasily Vasil'yvich. (1899). *Filo ogicheskoye Obozreniye, Moskva*, XVI (Part II). This citation never verified by the editor.

——————(1900). *Izvestiya drevnikh pisateley Grecheskikh i Latinskikh o Skifii i Kavkaze* [Information by Ancient Greek and Latin Authors on Scythia and the Caucasus]. St. Petersburg. Vol I, issue 8.

——————(1947, 1948, 1949). "Izvestiya drevnikh pisateley o Shifii i Kavkaze" [Information by Ancient Authors on Scythia and the Caucasus], prilozheniye [supplement to], *Akademiya Nauk, Institut Istorii, Vestnik Drevney Istorii*, I (1947), 253-316; II, 247-332; III, 235-315; IV, 169-291; I (1948), 221-317; II, 213-314; III, 215-330; IV, 223-298; I (1949), 183-295; II, 271-356; III, 203-308; IV, 227-305.

Lelewell, Joachim. (1852-1857). *Géographie du Moyen-âge*. Bruxelles. 4 vols.
Facsimile edition. Amsterdam: Meridian Publishing Co., 1967.

Leszczycki, Stanislaw and Bozena Modelska-Strzelecka (1967). "Six Centuries of Geography at the Jagellonian University in Cracow," *Geographica Polonica*, II, 5-28.

Lewicki, Tadeusz. (1945) (1954). *Polska i kraje sąsiednie w świetle "Księgi Rogera"*. Kraców: Polska Akademia Umiejętności, Prace Komisji Orientalistycznej; Warszawa: Prace Orientalist.

————— (1949-1950). "Świat stowiański w oczach pisarzy arabskich," *Slavia Antiqua*, II.

————— (1956). *Źródla arabskie do dziejów Slowiańszczyzny*. Wroclaw-Kraców: Źródla orientalne.

————— (1958). "Źródla arabskie i hebrajskie do dziejów Slowian w okresgie wczesnego średniowiecza," *Studia Źródloznawcze*, III.

L'Honore Naber, Samuel Pierre. (1917). *Reizen van Willem Barents, Jacob van Heemskerck, Jan Cornelisz, Rijp en anderen naar het Noorden*. 's-Gravenhage.

Longhena, Mario. (1929). *Viaggi in Persia, India e Giava di Nicolò de 'Conti*. Milano.

Longhena, Mario, and Pullè Francesco L. (1907). *Mappamondo Catalono della Estense* . . . Modena: Pellegrino Orlandini & Figli.

————— (1908). "Illustrazione del Mappamondo catalano della Biblioteca Estense di Modena," *Sesto Congresso Geografico Italiano, Venezia, Atti*, II, 341-397.

Lucas, F. W. (1898). *The Annals of the Voyages of the Brothers Nicolo and Antonio Zeno in the North Atlantic about the end of the Fourteenth Century and the Claim founded thereon to a Venetian Discovery of America*. London.

Magnaghi, Alberto. (1898). *La Carta Nautica constuita nel 1325 da Angelino Dalorto*. Firenze: Tip. di M. Ricci.

————— (1899). "Il mappamondo del Genovese Angellinus de Dalorto (1325)," *Terzo Congresso Geografico Italiano, Firenze, Atti*, II. 506-543.

Magnocavallo, A. (1902). "La carta "de mari mediterraneo" di Marin Sanudo "Il Vecchio"," *Societa Geografica Italiana, Roma: Bolletino*, III (Ser. IV), 438-449.

————— (1903). *Dialcuni codici del Liber Secretorum Fidelium Crucis di Marin Sanudo il Vecchio*. Venezia.

Malein, A. I. (1908). *Zapiski o moskovitskikh delakh. Pavel Ioviy Novokomskiy kniga o moskovitskom posol'stve* [Notes on Russia. Pavel Ioviy Novokomskiy's Text on the Muscovite Embassy]. St. Petersburg: A. S. Suvorin.

Manzi, Luigi. (1900). *Il Secolo Illustrato della Domenica* (Milano), September 23, p. 300. Reprinted by Crivellari, Giuseppe. *Alcuni cimeli della cartografia medievale esistenti a Verona*. Firenze: B. Seeber, 1903.

Marcel, Gabriel Alexander. (1896). *Choix de Cartes et de Mappemondes des XIVe et XVe siècles*. Paris: Ernest Leroux.

Markham, Sir Clements Robert. ed. (1912). *Book of the Knowledge of all kingdoms, lands, and lordships that ate in the world*, . . . London: The Haklyut Society.

Materialy (1871) = *Materialy dlya istoriko,geograficheskago Atlasa Rossii* [Material for an Historical-Geographical Atlas of Russia]. St. Petersburg: Izdatel'stvo Imperatorskoy Arkheograficheskoy Kommissii.

Metelka, Jindrich. (1895). "o mape Kard. Mikuláse cusy z prostredka XV století," *Vestník Královské Ceské Spolecnosti Náuk, Trída Filosoficko-Historiko-Jazykozpytna*, III.

Michow, H. (1882-1883). *Die ältesten Karten von Russland*," *Geographischen Gesellschaft in Hamburg: Mitteilungen*, 100-187.

Facsimile editions. See Michow (1962) and *Acta Cartographica*, III (1968), 325-417.

————— (1885). "Das Bekanntwerden Russlands in vor-Herberstein'scher zeit, ein Kampf zwischen Autorität und Wahrheit," *Verhandlungen des Fünften Deutschen Geographentages zu Hamburg*, 119-130.

————— (1892). "Caspar Vopell, ein Kölner Kartenzeichner des 16. Jahrhunderts," *Hamburgische Festschrift zur Erinnerung an die Entdeckung Amerika's*, I (#4), 5-22.

Facsimile edition. *Acta Cartographica*, I (1967), 280-297.

————— (1905). *Anton Wied, ein Danziger Kartograph des 16. Jahrhunderts*. Hamburg.

————— (1906). "Das erste Jahrhundert russicher Kartographie 1525-1631 und die Originalikarte des Anton Weid von 1542." *Geographische Gesellschaft in Hamburg: Mitteilungen*. XXI, 1-61.

————— (1907). "Weitere Beiträge zur älteren Kartographie Russlands," *Geographische Gesellschaft in Hamburg, Mitteilungen*. XXII, 125-172.

————— (1910). "Zur Geschichte der Bekanntschaft mit Sibirien vor Jermak," *Anthropologische Gesellschaft in Wien: Mitteilungen*, 1-21.

————— (1962). "Die ältesten Karten von Russland, ein Beitrag zur historichen Geographie. Amsterdam: Meridian Publishing Co,

Miller, Konrad. (1895-98). *Mappaemundi. Die ältesten Weltkarten*. Stuttgart: Jos. Roth'sche Verlagshandlung.

————— (1916). *Itineraria Romana. Römische Reisewegen an der Hand der Tabula Peutingeriana*. Stuttgart: Strecker und Schröder.

————— (1926-1931). *Mappae Arabicae; Arabische Welt-und Ländkarten des 9-13. Jahrhunderts* . . . Stuttgart: Selbstverlag des Herausgebers.

————— (1929). *Die Peutingersche Tafel; oder, Weltkarte des Castorius*, . . . Stuttgart: Strecker und Schröder.

——————— (1931). *Die ältesten Separatkarten der drei Erdteile, wahrscheinlich von Nikephorus Gregoras um 1350 in Konstantinopel entworfen.* Stuttgart: Selbstverlag des Herausgebers.

Minns, Ellis Hovel. (1913). *Scythians and Greeks; a Survey of Ancient History and Archaeology on the North Coast of the Euxine from the Danube to the Caucasus.* Cambridge: University Press.

Minorsky, Vladimir Fedorovich. (1937). *Hudud al-'Alam, "The Regions of the World;" a Persian Geography, 372 A.H. (982 A.D.).* London: Luzac & Co. "E. J. W. Gibb Memorial" Series, New Series, XI.

Mlodziejowski, J. (1947). "Zachodnie ziemie Polski na mapach XVIw," *Przegląd Zachodni,* III (#1), 323-332.

Moir, A. L. (1970). *The World Map in Hereford Cathedral.* Hereford: The Cathedral.

Molmenti, Pompeo. (1927). *La Storia di Venezia nella Vita Privata.* Bergamo: Ist. Italiana d'Arti Grafiche.

Morgan, Edward Delmar, & Coote, Charles Henry. (1886). *Early Voyages and Travels to Russia and Persia. . . .* London: The Hakluyt Society. 2 Vols.
.*Facsimile edition.* New York: Burt Franklin, 1968.

Müller, Carl. (1855). *Geographi Graeci Minores.* Paris.
Facsimile edition. Hildesheim: G. Olms, 1965.

Müller, Frederick. (1878). "De Kaart van Barendts," *Nederlandsch Aardrijkskondig Genootschap, Amsterdam: Tijdschrift,* III, 271.

Münster, Sebastian. (1588). *C. Julii Solini Polyhistor, Pomponii Melae de Situ Orbis libri tres.* Basileae.

Mzik, Hans von. (1915). "Ptolemäeus und die Karten der arabischen Geographen," *Geographische Gesellschaft in Wien: Mitteilungen,* LVIII (#3), 152-176.

——————— (1916). "Africa nach arabischen Bearbeitung . . . ," *Akademie der Wissenschaften: Wien, Philosophisch-Historische Klasse: Denkschriften,* LIX (Abhandlung 4), 1-55.

——————— (1926). "Das Kitab surat al-ard des Abu Gafar Muhammad ibn musa al-Huwarizmi," *Bibliothek Arabischer Historiker und Geographen,* III.

——————— (1936). "Osteuropa nach der arabischen Bearbeitung der . . . ," *Wiener Zietschrift für die Kunde des Morgenlandes, Wien,* XLIII (#3 & #4), 161-193.

——————— (1938). "Des Klaudios Ptolemäeus Einführung in die darstellende Erdkunde," *Klotho, Historische Studien zur Feudalen und Vorfeudalen Welt,* V, erster Teil.

Nehring, A. (1897c). "Einige Bemerkungen Über Anton Wieds "Moscovia" und das zugehörige Urusbild," *Globus, Illustrierte Zeitschrift für Länder und Völkerkunde,* LXXI, 85-89.

Neumann, Karl Johannes. (1884). "Die Fahrt des Patrokles auf dem Kaspischen Meere und der alte Lauf des Oxos," *Hermes, Zeitschrift für Klassische Philologie,* XIX, 165-185.

Nevgebaver, S. (1612). *Moscovia. Hoc est, de origine, situ regionibus, moribus, religione, ac Republicae Moscoviae Commentarius.* Gedani.

Nissen, Kristian. (1941). "Nordenskartet fra 1532. . . . ," *Saertrykk av Morgenbladet,* December 13 and 16 (#291 and 293).

——————— (1956). "Jacob Ziegler's Palestine Schondia Manuscript, University Library, Olso, NS. 917-4°," *Imago Mundi,* XIII, 45-52.

Nordenskiöld, A. E. (1882). *Umsegelung Asiens und Europas.* Leipzig.

——————— (1885). *Studien und Forschungen veranlasst durch meine Reisen im hohen Norden.* Leipzig.

——————— (1889). *Facsimile Atlas to the Early History of Cartography . . .* Trans. Johan Adolf Ekelöf and Clements R. Markham. Stockholm.
Facsimile edition: New York: Kraus Reprint Corp., 1961.

——————— (1891). "Om ett aftryck från XV: de seklet af den i metall graverade världskarta, som förvarats i Kardinal Stephan Borgias Museum I Velletri," *Ymer,* XI, 83-92.
Facsimile edition. Acta Cartographica, V (1939), 356-365).

——————— (1897). *Periplus. An Essay on the Early History of Charts and Sailing Directions.* Trans. Francis A. Bather. Stockholm.
Facsimile edition. New York: Burt Franklin Research and Source Works Series #52, 1964.

Nunn, George Emra. (1929). *Origin of the Strait of Anian Concept.* Philadelphia: Private Printing.

Olszewicz, Boleslaw. (1930). "Kartografja Polska XV i XVI Wieku," *Polski Przegląd Kartograficzny,* Tom IV, Rok VIII (#31), 147-168.

Ongania, Ferdinand, (ed.). (1881). *Raccolta di Mappamondi.* Venezia: Ferdinand Ongania. 10 Vols.

Ortroy, F. Van (1892-1893). "L'oeuvre géographique de Mercator," *Société Scientifique de Bruxelles: Revue des Questions Scientifiques,* II (Oct.), 507-571; III (Apr.), 556-582.

——————— (1914-1916). "Bibliographie sommaire de L'Oeuvre Mercatorienne," *Association des Bibliothécaires Français: Revue des Bibliothèques,* XXIV, 113-148; XXV-XXVI, 9-30, 119-141.

Paleolog, M. (1853). "Peripl Skilakhsa Kariandskago" [The Periplus of Sylax of Karyanda], *Odesskoye Obshchestvo Istorii i Drevnostey, Zapiski,* III, 130-143.

Palmén, E. G. (1912). "Simon van Salinghens karta öfver norden 1601," *Fennia*, XXXI (#6), 1-10.

Panagiodor-Nikovul, A. (1848). "Bezimyannago Peripl Ponta Yevsinskago i Meotiyskago Ozera" [Of the Unnamed Navigational Guides of the Black Sea & Sea of Azov], *Odesskoye Obshchestvo Istorii i Drevnostey, Zapiski*, II, 232-244.

Peschel, O. (1871). *Der Atlas des Andrea Bianco vom Jahre 1436*. München, Venedig.

Platonov, C. F. (1922). *Moskva i Zapad* [Moscow and Western Europe].

Polaschek, Erich (1959). "Ptolemy's Geography in a New Light," *Imago Mundi*, XIV, 17-37.

Potocki, Jan. (1796). *Mémoire sur un nouveau peryple du Pont Euxin, ainsi que sur la plus ancienne histoire des peuples du Taurus, du Caucase, et de la Scythie*. Vienna: Matthias André Schmidt.

Pullé, Francesco L. (1901, 1905). "La Cartografia Antica dell'India," *Studi Italiani di Filologia Indo-Iranica*, Florence, Part 1: V, 1-221, Part II: IX, 1-387.

Quad, Matthias. (1594). *Evropae Totv is Orbis Terrarvm Partis Praestantissimae, Vniversalis et Particvlaris Descriptio* . . . Coloniae: Jani Bussemechers.

Remarkable Maps (1894, 1895, 1897) = *Remarkable Maps of the XVth, XVIth, & XVIIth Centuries Reproduced in Their Original Size*. Amsterdam: Frederick Muller & Co. 6 vols.

Richter, Herman (ed.). (1936). "Orbis Arctoi nova et accurata Delineatio. Auctore Andrea Bureo Sueco 1626," *Lund Universität, Geografiska Institution, Meddelanden, Avhandlingar, III*.

Roersch, Alphonse. (1910). *L'Humanisme Belga, à l'époque de la Renaissance; études et portraits*. Bruxelles: G. van Oest & Co.

Rostovtsev, Mikhail Ivanovich. (1918). *Éllinstvo i Iranstvo na yuge Rossii* [Greeks and Iranians in South Russia]. Petrograd: 1918.

——————— (1922). *Iranians and Greeks in South Russia*. Oxford: The Clarendon Press.

——————— (1925). *Skifiya i Bosfor* [Scythia and the Bosphorus]. Leningrad: 1925.

Rovinsky, Dmitrii Aleksandrovich. (1882). *Dostovernẏye portretẏ moskovskikh gosudarey* [Authentic Portraits of Muskovite Monarchs]. St. Petersburg:

Ruge, Sophus. (1891). "Ein Jubiläum der deutschen Kartographie," *Globus, Illustrierte Zeitschrift für Länder und Völkerkunde*, LX, 4-8.

Russkaya Letopis' (1767-1790). = *Russkaya Letopis' po Nikonovu Spisku* [Russian Chronicles According to the Nikonov Chronicle]. Sankpeterburg: Akademiya Nauk, 6 vols.

Rẏbakov, B. A. (1952). "Russkiye zemli po karte Idrici 1154 goda" [Russian Lands on the Map of Idrisi of 1154], *Akademiya Nauk, Institut Istorii Material'noy Kul'turẏ. Kratkiye Soobshcheniya*, (#43), 1-44.

Santarem, Manuel Francisco. (1842-1853). *Atlas, compose de Mappemondes, de Portulans, et de Cartes hydrographiques et historiques, depuis le VIe jusqu'au XVIIe siècle*, . . . Paris:

——————— (1849, 1850, 1852). *Essai sur l'histoire de la Cosmographie et de la Cartographie pendant le Moyen-Age, et sur les Progrès de la Géographie après les Grandes Découvertes du XVe siècle*. Paris: Maulde et Renou.

Schnabel, Paul. (1930). *Die Entstehungsgeschichte des kartographischen Erdbildes des Klaudios Ptolemaios*. Berlin.

——————— (1938). *Text und Karten des Ptolemäeus*. Leipzig: K. F. Koehlers Antiquarium.

Schultheiss, Dr. Fr. Guntram von. (1894). "Das Geographische in Hartmenn Schedels Liber Cronicarum 1493," *Globus, Illustratrierte Zeitschrift für Länder und Völkerkunde*, LXV, 6-11, 27-32.

Schütte, G. (1917). *Ptolemy's Maps of Northern Europe*. Kobenhavn.

Seroux d'Agincourt, Jean Baptiste Louis George. (1811-1823). *Histoire de l'art par les monuments, depuis sa décadence au 4e siècle* . . . Paris.

Serristori, Luigi. (1856). *Illustrazione diuna Carta del Mar Nero del MCCCLI e ricordi sul Caucaso, sulla Spagna, sul Marocco, etc.* Firenze.

Shcheglov, D. F. (1876). "Pervẏya stranitsẏ russkoy istorii" [The First Pages of Russian History], *Ministerstvo Narodnago Prosveshcheniya, Zhurnal*, #184, 221-269.

Shumovskiy, Feodor Adamovich. (1957). *Ahmad ibn Majid al Sa'di* . . . Moskva: Izd-vo Akad. Nauk.

Simonsfield, H. (1881). "Studien zu Marino Sanuto dem Älteren," *Gesellschaft für ältere deutsche Geschichtskunde: Neues Archiv*, VII (#4), 43-72.

Skelton, R. A. (1952). *Decorative Printed Maps of the 15th to 18th Centuries*. London: Staples Press.

Skelton, R. A., Thomas E. Marston, and George D. Painter. (1965). *The Vinland Map and the Tartar Relation*. New Haven: Yale University Press.

Sobko, N. P. (1881 & 1886). "Drevniya izobrazheniya russkikh Tsarey i ikh posol'stv za granitsu v starẏkh i novẏkh gravyurakh" [Representations of Russians Tsars and Their Embassies to Foreign Lands on Old and New Engravings], *Leningrad Arkheologicheskiy Institut, Sbornik*, V (#1, 1881, otd II), 237-332; V (#2, 1886, otd II), 333-412.

Sommerbradt, Ernst. (1891). *Die Ebstorfer Weltkarte*. Hannover: Hahn'sche Buchhandlung.

Spasskiy, Grigoriy Ivanovich. (1846). *Bosfor Kimmeriyskiy s yego drevnostyami i dostopamyatnostyami* [The Cimmerian Bosphorus], Moskva: Universitetskoy Tipografii.

Spekke, Arnolds. (1948). "A Brief Cartographic-Iconographic View of the Eastern Baltic Coast up to the 16th Century," *Imago Mundi*, V, 39-52.

Stahl, William H. (1951). "A Forthcoming Bibliography of Ptolemy's Geography," *Imago Mundi*. VIII, 26.

Stanford, E. (1869). *Hanc quam videtis terram orbis tabulam descripsit delineavitque Bicardus de Haldingham sive de Bello dictur. A. S. circa 1300*. London.

Steger, E. (1896). "Untersuchungen über italienische Seekarten des Mittelalters auf Grund der Kartometrischen Methode," *Report of the Sixth International Geographical Congress in London, 1895*.

Stevenson, Edward Luther (ed.). (1911a). *Atlas of Portolan Charts. Facsimile of a Manuscript in The British Museum*. New York: The Hispanic Society of America. (Egerton Manuscript #2803 in British Museum).

———————— (1911b). *Portolan Charts. Their origin and characteristics, with a descriptive list of those belonging to the Hispanic Society of America*. New York: The Hispanic Society of America.

———————— (1912). *Genoese World Map, 1457, Facsimile*. New York: The American Geographical Scoiety and The Hispanic Society of America.

———————— (ed.). (1932). *Geography of Claudius Ptolemy*. New York: The New York Public Library.

Sykes, Godfrey. (1915). "The Mythical Straits of Anian," *Bulletin of the American Geographical Society*, XLVII, 161-172.

Tallgren-Tuulio, O. J. (1936). "Du Nouveau Sur Idrisi," *Studia Orientalia, Helsingfors*, VI (#3), 1-240.

Tallgren-Tuulio, O. J., & Tallgren, A. M. (1930). "Idrisi, La Finlande et les autres pays Baltiques Orientaux," *Studia Orientalia, Helsingfors*, III, 3-157.

Taylor, E. G. R. (1955). "John Dee and the Map of North-East Asia," *Imago Mundi*, XII, 103-106.

Tcharykow, N. (1905). "Le Chevalier Barberini chez le Tsar Ivan le Terrible," *Revue d'Histoire (et) Diplomatique*.

Thomas, Georg Martin. (1864). "Der Periplus des Pontus Euxinus nach Müchener, Handschriften," *Bayerische Akademie der Wissenschaften, Müchen, Philosophisch-Philogischen Classe: Abhandlungen*, X, 221-290.

Tooley, R. V. (1939). "Maps in Italian Atlases of the Sixteenth Century," *Imago Mundi*, III, 12-47.

———————— (1952). *Maps and Map Makers*. New York: Bonanza Books.

Uhden, Richard von. (1932). "Bemerkungen zu dem römischen Kartenfragment con Dura Europas," *Hermes, Zeitschrift für Klassische Philologie*, LXVII, 117-125.

———————— (1935). "Die antieken Grundlagen der mittelalterlichen Seekarten," *Imago Mundi*, I, 1-19.

Uzielli, Gustavo, and Amat di san Filippo, Pietro. (1882). "Mappamondi, carte nautiche, portulani ed altri monumenti cartografici specialmente Italiani dei secali XIII-XVII," *Società Geografica Italiana, Studi Bibliografici e Biografici*, II.

Veen, Adrian (1597). *Napasser van de westersche ende oostersche Zee-vaert*. Amsterdam:

Vincent, William, Dean of Westminster. (1807). *The Commerce and Navigation of the Ancients in the Indian Ocean*. London: T. Cadell & W. Davies. 2 Vols.

———————— (1808). *On the Map of Fra Mauro and V. Bellemo, La cosmografia e la scoperti geografiche nel secolo XVe i viaggi di Nicolo de Conti*. Padua.

Vizye, V. Yu. (1948a). "*Villem Barents (k 350-letiyu so dnya smerti)*" [Wilhelm Barents (Three Hundred and Fifty Years Since His Death)] *Vsesoyuznoye Geograficheskoye Obshchestvo, Izvestiya*, LXXX (#4), 340-345.

Vyazemski, Pavel Petrovich. (1873). *Zamechaniya na Slovo o Pl''ku Igorev Knyazya II*. [Observations on the Lay of Prince Igor II's Host].

Wagner, Henry R. (1931). "The Manuscript Atlases of Battista Agnese . . . ," *Bibliographical Society of America, Papers*, XXV, 1-110.

———————— (1947). "Additions to the Manuscript Atlases of Battista Agnese," *Imago Mundi*, IV, 28-30.

Wagner, Hermann. (1885). "Patrocles am Karabugas," *Geographische Nachrichten*, p. 209. This citation not verified by the editor.

———————— (1896). "Das Rätsel der Kompasskarten im Lichte der Gesamtentwickelung der Seekarten," *Deutschen Geographentages zu Bremen: Verhandlungen*, 65-87.

Westberg, Friedrich. (1903). *Kommentariy na zapisku Ibragima Ibn-Yakuba o slavyanakh* [Commentary on Ibrahim Ibn-Jakub's Note on the Slavonians]. St. Peterburg: Tip. Imperatorskoy Akademii Nauk.

Wieder, F. C. (1925-1933). *Monumenta Cartographica*. The Hague: Martinus Nijhoff. 6 Vols.

Wieser, Franz Ritter von. (1912). *Die Weltkarte des Albertin de Virga aus dem Anfange des 15. Jahrhunderts in der Sammlung Figdor in Wien*. Innsbruck: H. Schwick.

Wilson, Francesca. (1970). *Muscovy: Russia Through Foreign Eyes, 1553-1900*. London: George Allen & Unwin Ltd.

Winter, Heinrich. (1940). "Das Katalanische Problem in der älteren Kartographie," *Ibero-Amerikanisches Archiv, Berlin*, XIV (Heft 2/3, Juli/Oct), 89-126.

——————— (1942). "Die angebliche Toscanelli-Karte," *Koloniale Rundschau, Zeitschrift für koloniale Wirtschaft, Völker, und Länderkunde,* XXXIII (Dec.), 228-238.

——————— (1953). "A Circular Map in a Ptolemaic MS.," *Imago Mundi,* X, 15-22.

——————— (1962). "The Fra Mauro Portolan Chart in the Vatican," *Imago Mundi,* XVI, 17-28.

Wojciechowski, S. (1926). "Macie z Miechowa jako geograf. krajów litewakoruskich," *Uniwersytet Jagielloński,* Kraków: Kolo Geografów Uczniów, Sprawozdania, II, 120.

Wolkenhauer, August. (1904). "Beiträge zur Geschichte der Kartographie und Nautik des 15. bis 17. Jahrhunderts," *Geographische Gesellschaft in München: Mitteilungen,* I, 161-260.

——————— (1909). "Sebastian Münsters handschriftliches Kollegienbuch aus den Jahren 1515-1518 und seine Karten," *Akademie der Wissenschaften zu Göttingen, Philologisch-Historische Klasse: Abhandlungen,* XI (#3), 1-68. *Facsimile edition. Acta Cartographica,* VI (1969), 427-498.

Wright, John K. (1928). "The Leardo Map of the World 1452 or 1453," New York: American Geographical Society. Series No. 4.

Wuttke, Heinrich. (1870). "Zur Geschichte der Erdkunde in der letzten Hälfe des Mittelalters. Die Karten der seefahrden Völker Südeuporas bis zum ersten Druck der Erdbeschreibung des Ptolemäeus," *Vereins für Erdkunde zu Dresden, Jahresbericht,* VI und VII, 1-66.

Yefimov, A. V. (1948). *Iz istorii russkikh ėkspiditsiy na Tikhom Okeane pervaya polovina XVIII veka* [From the History of the Russian Expeditions on the Pacific Ocean in the First Half of the 18th Century]. Moskva: Voyennoye Izdatel'stvo Ministerstva vooruzhennýkh Sil Soyuza SSR.

——————— (ed.) (1964). *Atlas Geograficheskikh Otkrýtiy v Sibiri i v Severo-zapadnoy Amerike XVII-XVIIIvv.* [Atlas Geographical Discoveries in Siberia and Northwestern America]. Moskva: Izdatel'stvo "Nauka".

Yegorov, D. N. (1913). *Srednevekov'ye v yego pamyatnikah* [The Middle Ages in its Monuments]. Moskva: Tipo-Lit. Ya. Dankin i Ya. Khomutov.

Yusuf Kamal. Prince. (1926-1951). *Monumenta Cartographica Africae et Aegypti.* Cairo: 5 vols.

Zagorskiy, E. A. (1922). *Ocherk istorii Severnogo Prichernomorya* [An Essay on the History of the Northern Black Sea Area]. Odessa.

Zamýslovskiy, Ye. Ye. (1875). "Baron Sigizmund Herbershteyn i yego sochineniye o Rossii v XVI veke" [Baron Herberstein and His Work on Russia in the 16th Century], *Drevnyaya i Novaya Rossiya,* III, (#9), 41-55; (#10), 134-151; (#12), 316-334.

——————— (1876). "Geograficheskiye izvestiya Herbershteyna o moskovskoy Rusi" [Herberstein's Geographical Information on Muscovite Russia], *Drevnyaya i Novaya Rossiya,* (#10), 170-177; (#11), 250-255; (#12), 343-348.

——————— (1880b). "Opisaniye Litvý, Samogitii, Russii i Moskovii Sebastiana Münstera (16 veka)" [A Description of Lithuania, Russia, and Muscovy by Sebastian Münster (16th C.)], *Ministerstvo Narodnago Prosveshcheniya, Zhurnal,* CCXI (otd. 2), 66-123.

——————— (1884a). "Herbershteyn i yego istoriko-geograficheskiya izvestia o Rossii" [Herbertstein and His Historical-Geographical Information on Russia], *St. Petersburg Universitet, Istoriko-Filologicheskiy Fakul'tet, Zapiski,* XIII, 477-880.

Zourayev, A. P. (1966). *Severnýye Irantsý vostochnoy vevropý i severnogo Kavkaza* [North Iranians of East Europe and Northern Caucasia]. North Bergen, N. J.: Private Printing.

Zurla, Placido. (1806). *Il Mappamondo di Fra Mauro Camaldolese.* Venice.

INDEX

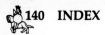